YOU CAN DO IT!
P 1.0

Implementation of projects on a breadboard

(1st Edition)

Published by
BG PRINTING HOUSE
Yangon, Myanmar.
Ph: +184 789 000 36, +951 945 006 1315
Email: suankap@gmail.com

CONTENTS

Acknowledgements

- *Almighty God has been guiding me until today*
- *All my family members who have always supported me*
- *All teachers who taught me*
- *U Kyaw Thu for giving advice and guidance to me*
- *Thar Pyih helped me with designs and photography*
- *Friends who gave me advice*

INTRODUCTION

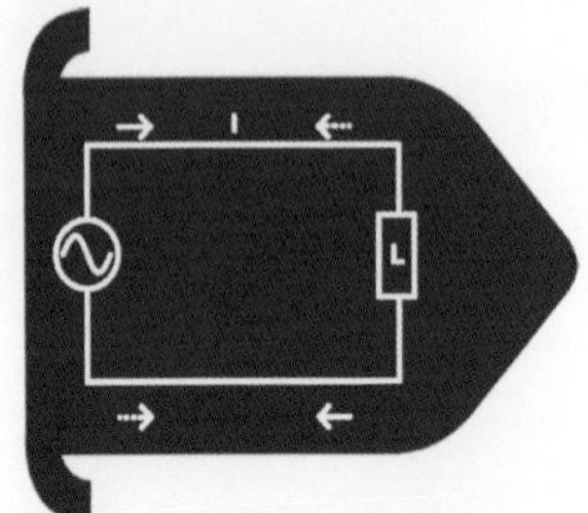

1. Alternating Current (AC Current)

A current in which electrons flow back and forth from east to west or from west to east at a regular period and a circle is called AC Current.

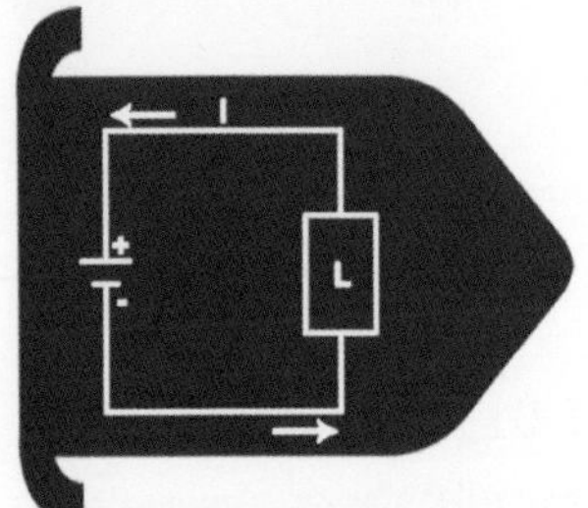

2. Direct Current (DC Current)

A current in which the electrons are flowing in only one direction is called DC Current. Although the intensity of the electric current may change over time, the general direction of the flow remains the same every time.

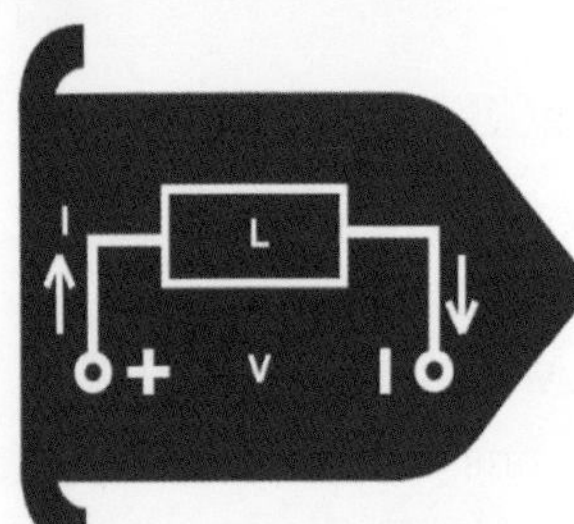

3. Ohm's Law

The voltage supplied to a conductor is directly proportional to the current passed over the conductor between two points.

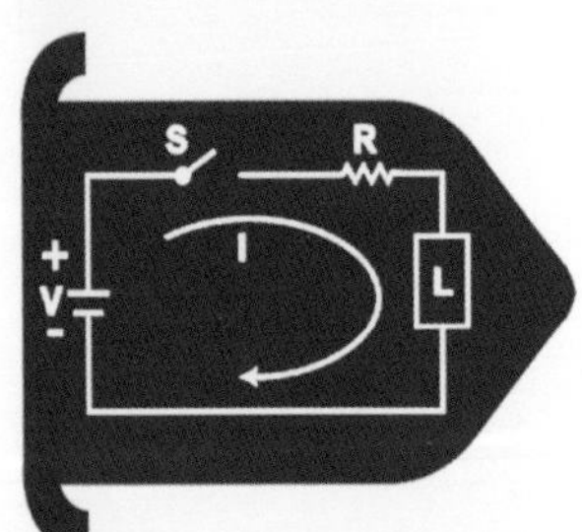

4. Electric Circuit

An electric current passing through a conductor and flowing in a complete path without interruption is called an Electric Circuit.

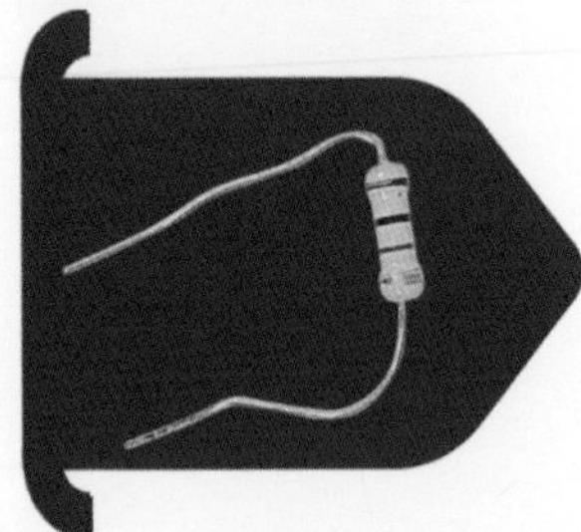

5. Resistor

A conductor that limits or regulates the flow of an electric current in an electric circuit is called a resistor.

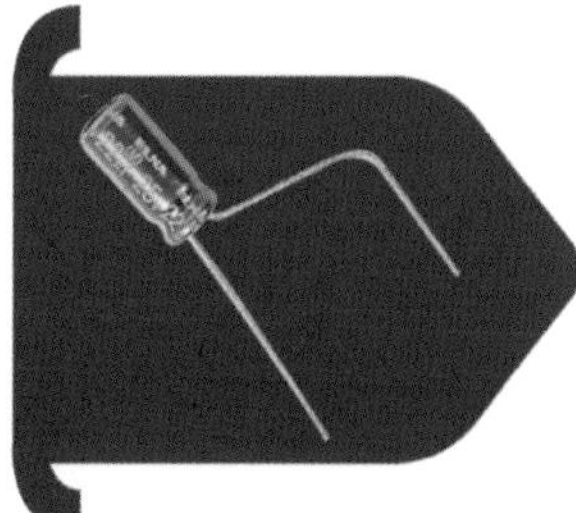

6. Capacitor

A capacitor can store electrical energy obtained from any energy source. It can maintain that electrical charge for a certain amount of time when the connection to the power source is lost. A capacitor is a passive electronic device.

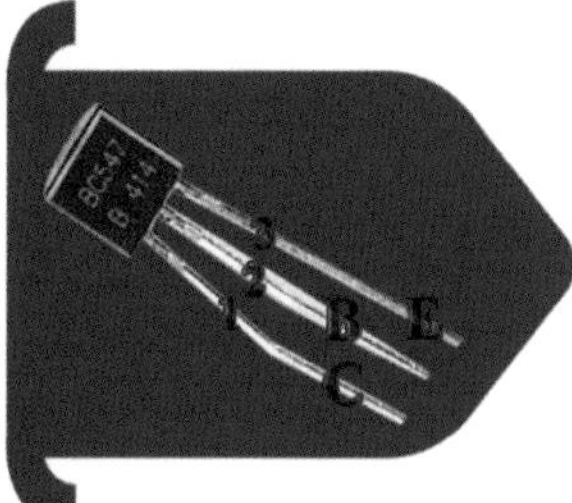

7. Transistor

A transistor is an electronic device or a semiconductor that partially resists electrical conduction. It consists of three pins (Collector, Emitter, and Base). Depending on the structure, there are BJT-type and FET-type.

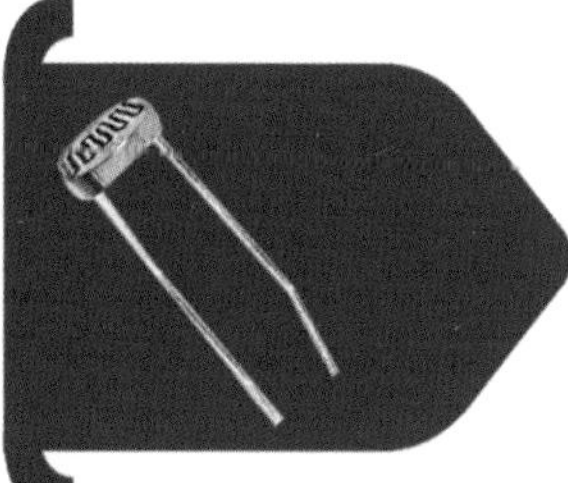

8. Light Dependent Resistor (LDR)

LDR is one type of resistor that changes the way the circuit works according to the light that falls on it. The LDR resistance value will decrease if more light falls on the LDR. The less light incident on the LDR, the higher the resistance value.

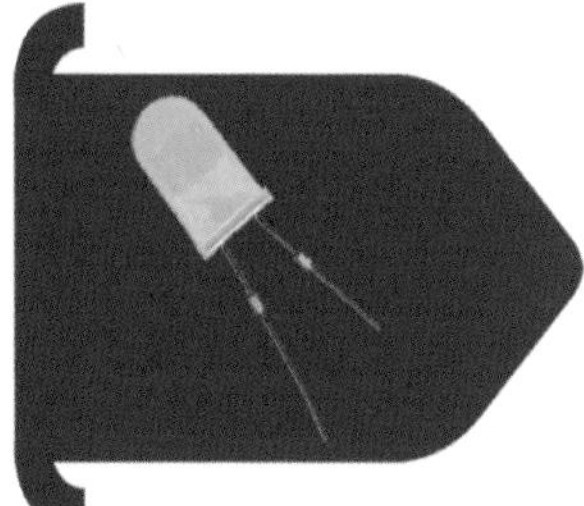

9. Light - emitting Diode (LED)

One semiconductor emits light when an electric current is flowing through it. That sort of semiconductor is called an LED, and the current flows in one direction because it is one type of diode. Usually, an LED has two pins. The longer pin is the Anode, and the shorter pin is the Cathode. The Cathode plate is larger than the Anode plate.

10. Battery

A battery is an energy source containing one or more chemical cells that convert chemical energy into electrical energy. At both ends of these cells, there are Anode and Cathode poles.

INTRODUCTION

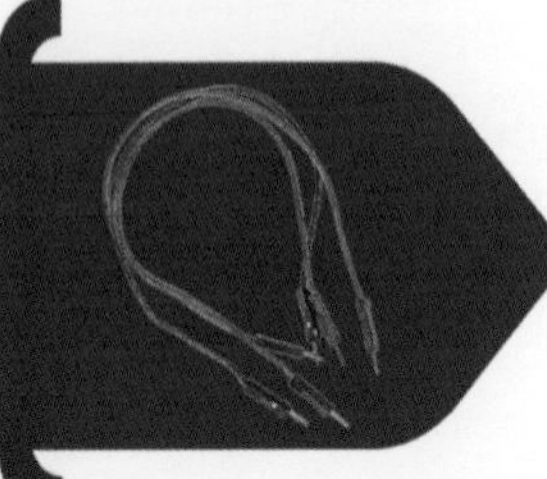

11. Jumper Wire

A jumper wire is a wire with pins attached to both ends of a wire so that it is easy to conduct electricity when implementing the project on a breadboard.

12. Breadboard

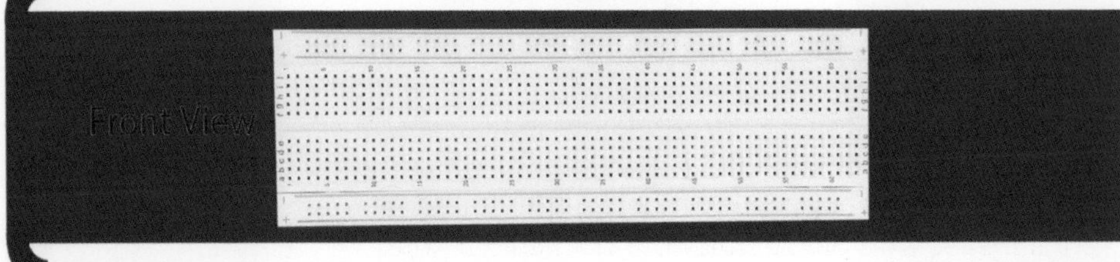

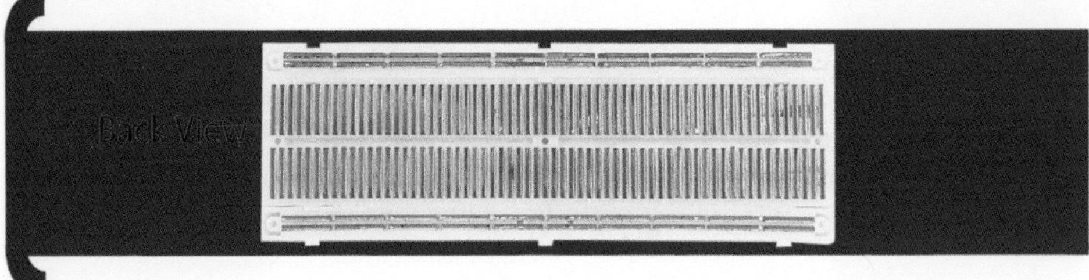

A breadboard is one electronic device designed to implement an electronic circuit without soldering the electronic components. The components can be easily removed, installed, and connected when implementing the project on the breadboard. The breadboard has many small vertical and horizontal holes. Horizontal holes have a single-row connection used to supply power. Vertical holes are connected to each row and used for placing electronic components. Vertical holes have no lateral contact. There are two sets of five rows of a vertical hole, and the set does not connect.

☞ **Other wires are used instead of Jumper Wire for visual clarity when demonstrating how the project works.**

PROJECT (1)
ONE LED CIRCUIT

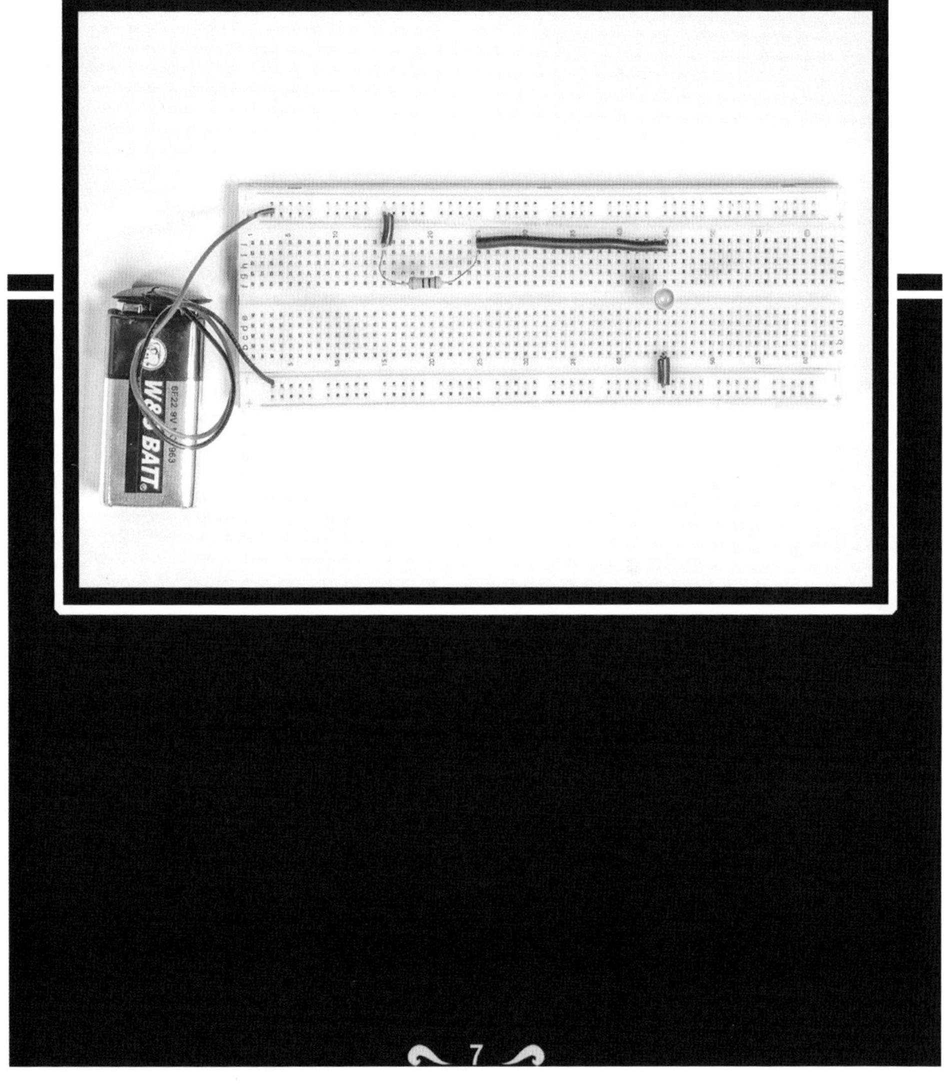

PROJECT (1)

COMPONENTS

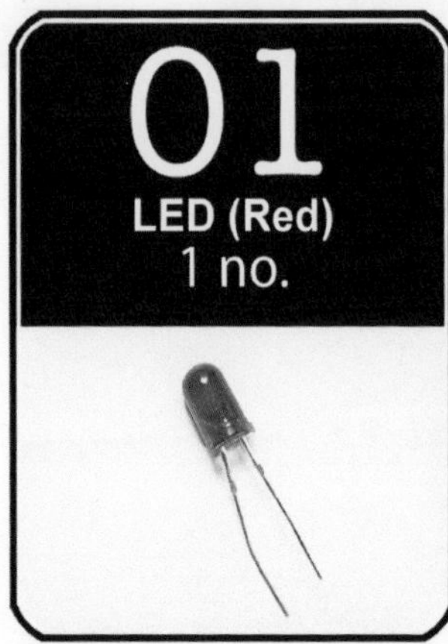

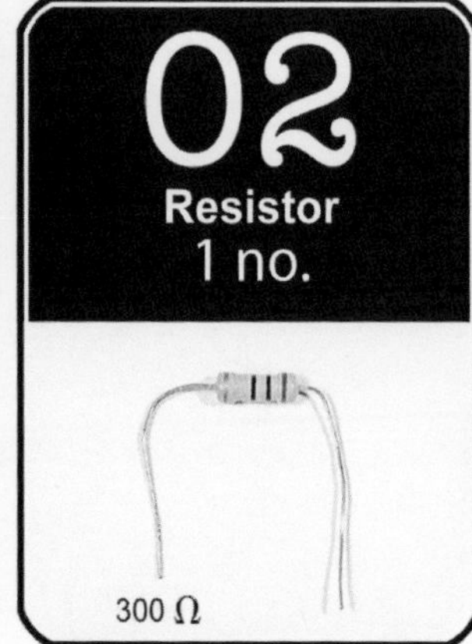

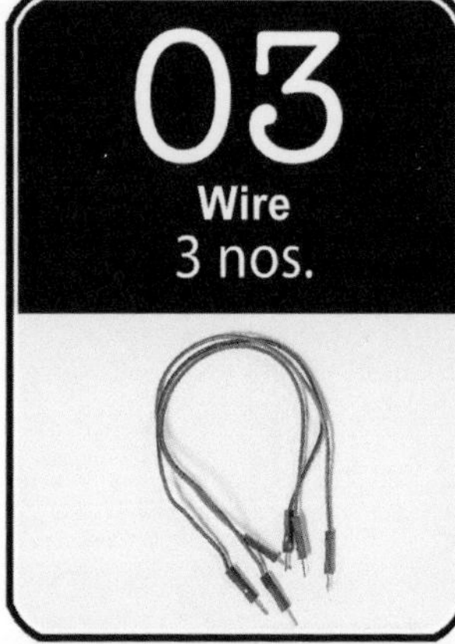

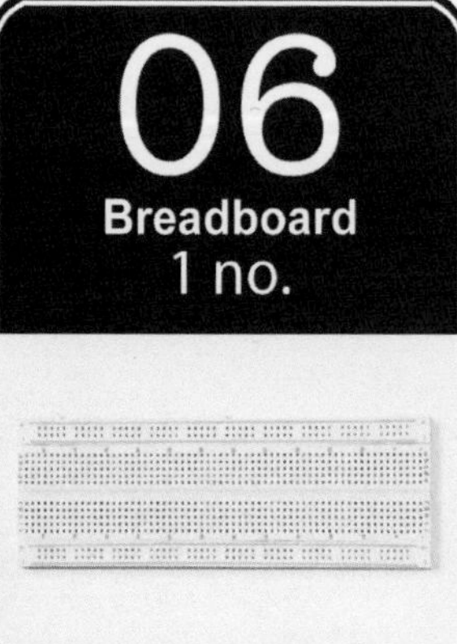

Steps of Implementation

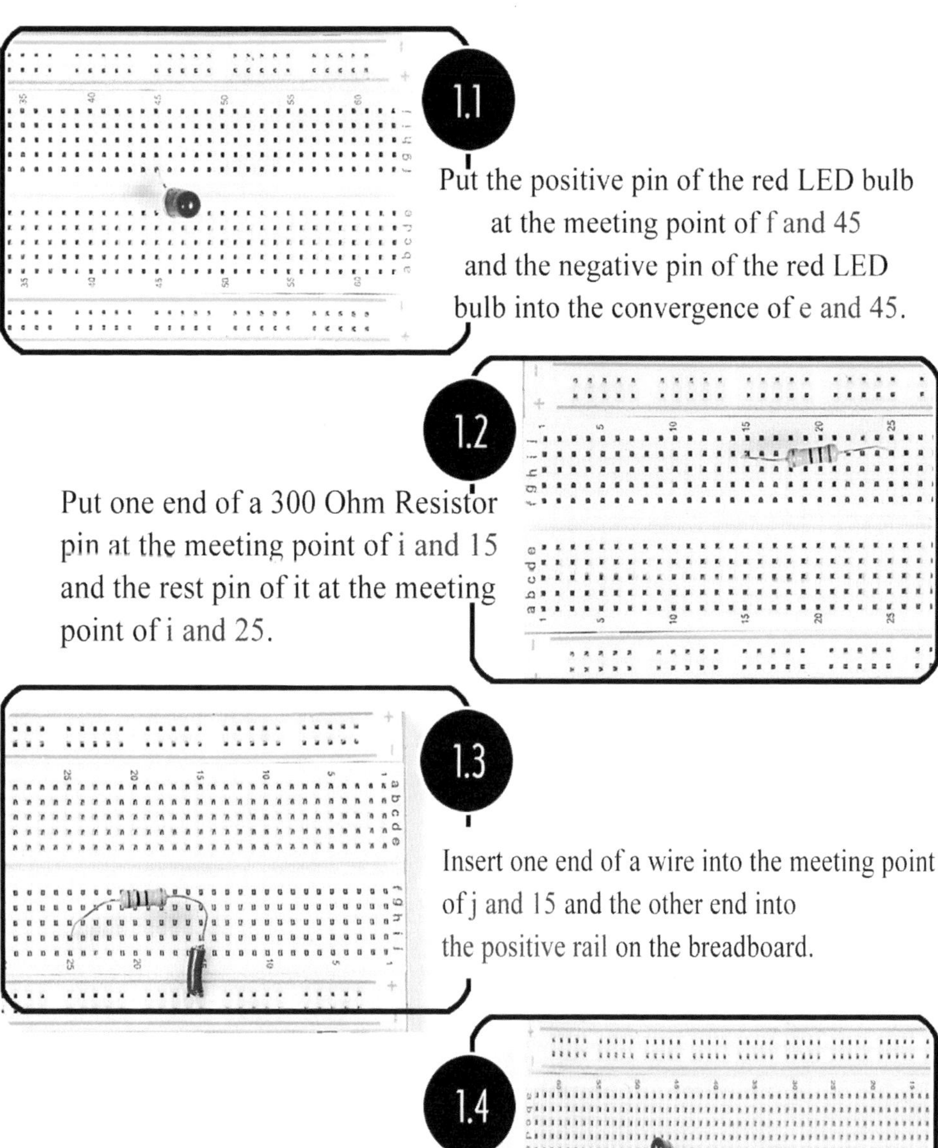

1.1

Put the positive pin of the red LED bulb at the meeting point of f and 45 and the negative pin of the red LED bulb into the convergence of e and 45.

1.2

Put one end of a 300 Ohm Resistor pin at the meeting point of i and 15 and the rest pin of it at the meeting point of i and 25.

1.3

Insert one end of a wire into the meeting point of j and 15 and the other end into the positive rail on the breadboard.

1.4

Insert one end of a wire into the meeting point of j and 25 and the other end into the meeting point of j and 45.

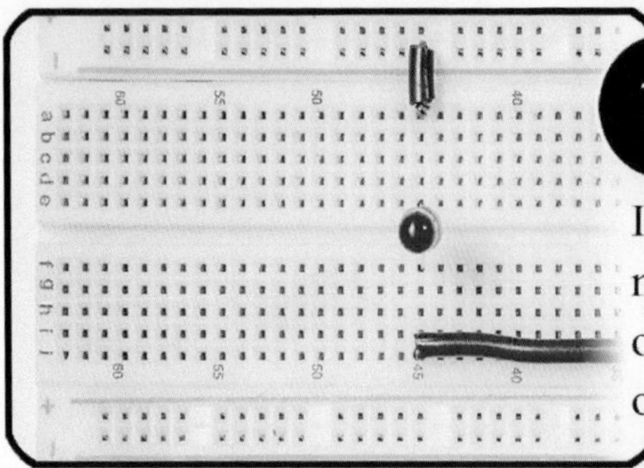

1.5

Insert one end of a wire into the meeting point of a and 45 and the other end into the negative rail on the breadboard.

1.6

Connect a 9V battery to the battery connector, and then connect the positive wire of the battery connector to the positive rail on the breadboard and the negative wire of the battery connector to the negative rail on the breadboard.

Explanation

Figures 1.1 to 1.2 are the placement of components.
Figures 1.3 to 1.6 are the figures of wiring the components.
When supplying the power through battery 9V,
the current will cross the resistor and flow to the LED light.
Through that, it reaches the ground,
and the circuit is complete, so the LED lights up.

PROJECT (2)
Two LEDs CONNECTED IN SERIES CIRCUIT

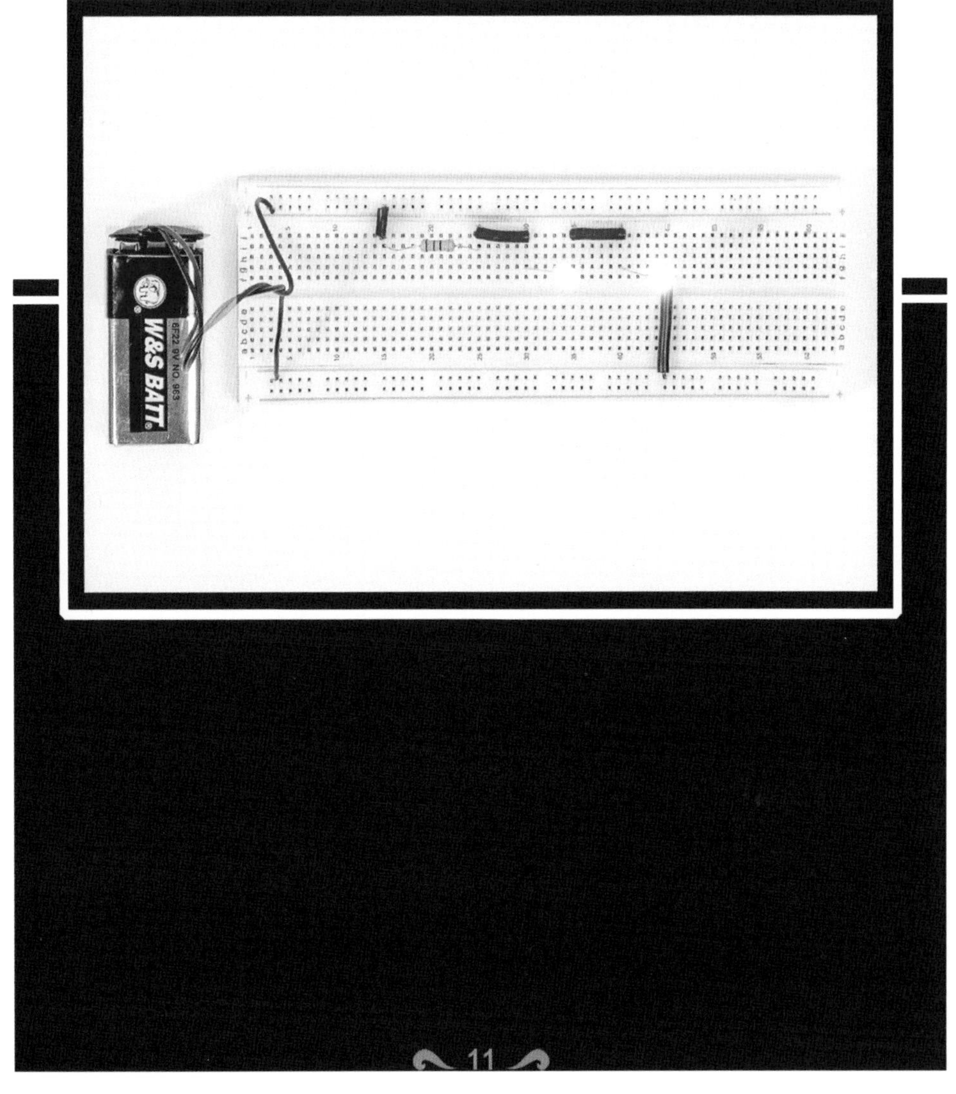

COMPONENTS

01
LED (White)
2 nos.

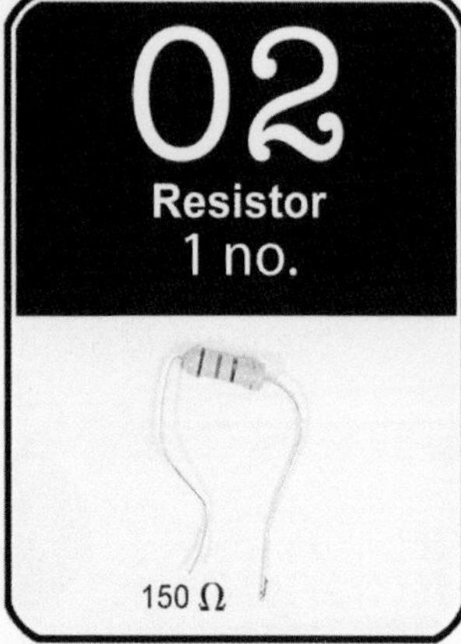

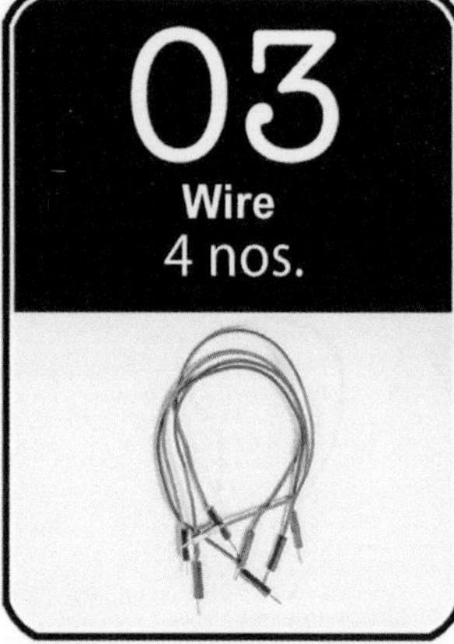

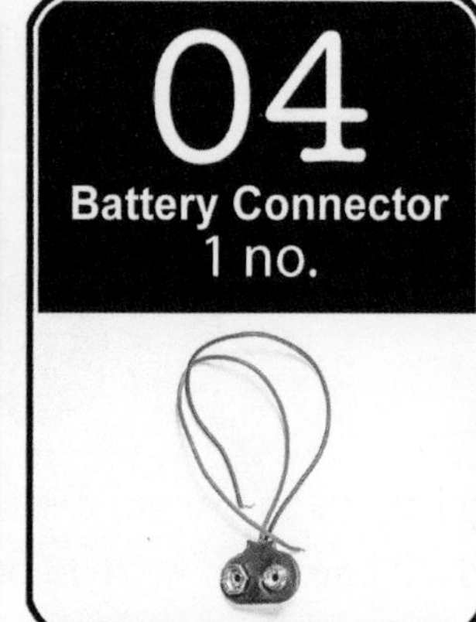

Steps of Implementation

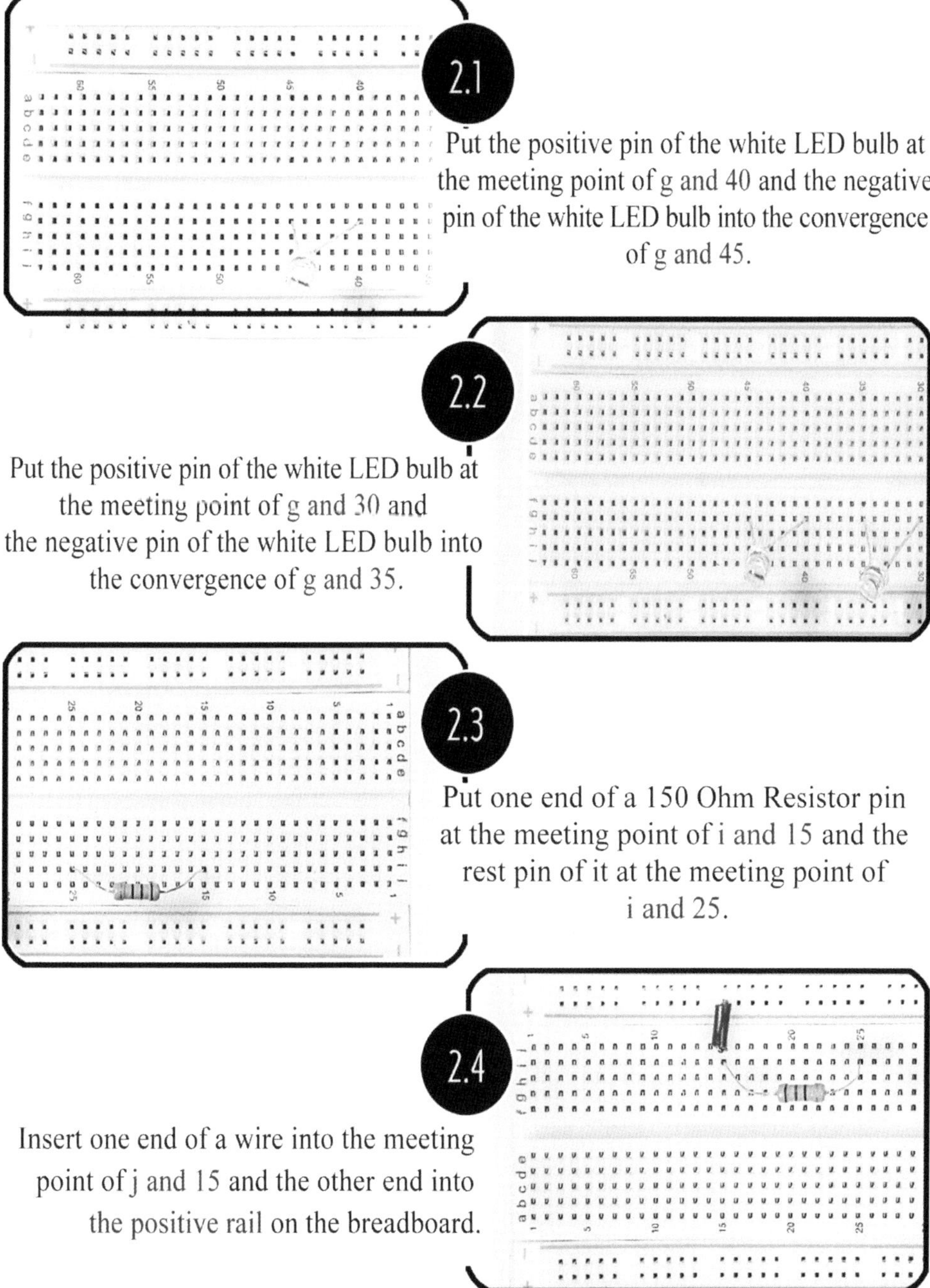

2.1

Put the positive pin of the white LED bulb at the meeting point of g and 40 and the negative pin of the white LED bulb into the convergence of g and 45.

2.2

Put the positive pin of the white LED bulb at the meeting point of g and 30 and the negative pin of the white LED bulb into the convergence of g and 35.

2.3

Put one end of a 150 Ohm Resistor pin at the meeting point of i and 15 and the rest pin of it at the meeting point of i and 25.

2.4

Insert one end of a wire into the meeting point of j and 15 and the other end into the positive rail on the breadboard.

PROJECT (2)

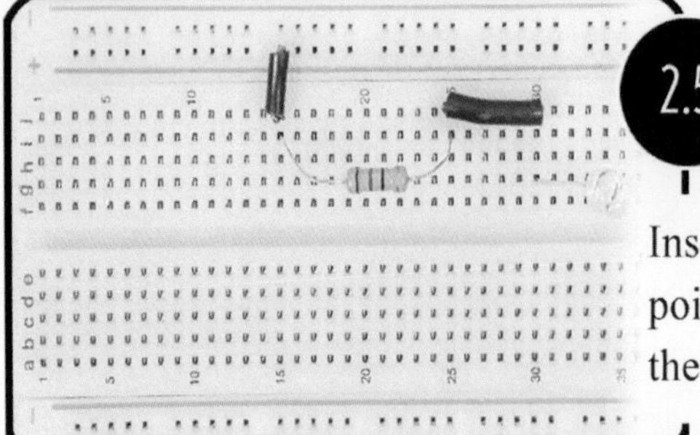

2.5

Insert one end of a wire into the meeting point of j and 25 and the other end into the meeting point of j and 30.

2.6

Insert one end of a wire into the meeting point of j and 35 and the other end into the meeting point of j and 40.

2.7

Insert one end of a wire into the meeting point of f and 45 and the other end into the negative rail on the breadboard.

2.8

Connect a 9V battery to the battery connector, and then connect the positive wire of the battery connector to the positive rail on the breadboard and the negative wire of the battery connector to the negative rail on the breadboard.

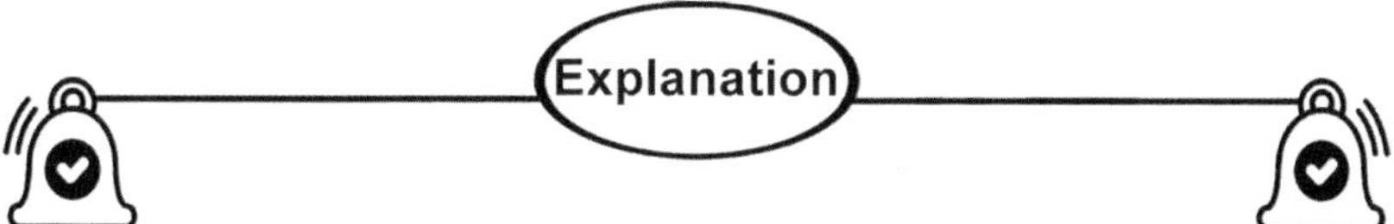

Figures 2.1 to 2.3 are the placement of components and Figures 2.4 to 2.8 are the figures of wiring the components. The two LEDs are connected in series to light up. Since the two LEDs are connected in series, if one LED goes off, the other one will not light up.

Series Circuit

A circuit in which the loads are being connected in a series is called a series circuit. In the series circuit, the amount of current flowing through each load is the same, and the sum of all the voltages supplied to each load equals the supply voltage.

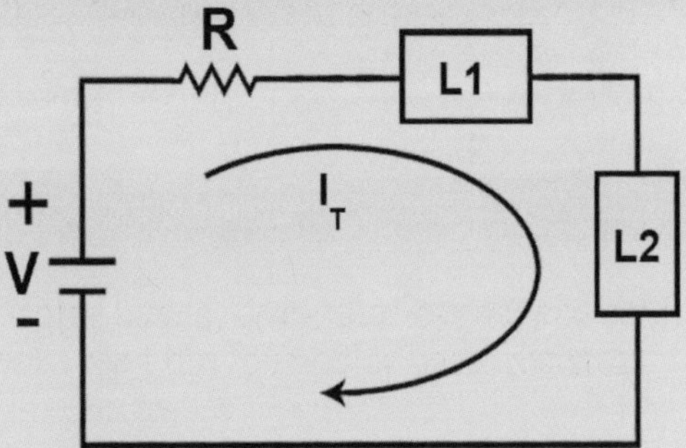

$$I_T = I_1 = I_2$$

$$V_T = V_1 + V_2$$

PROJECT (3)
Three LEDs
CONNECTED IN PARALLEL CIRCUIT

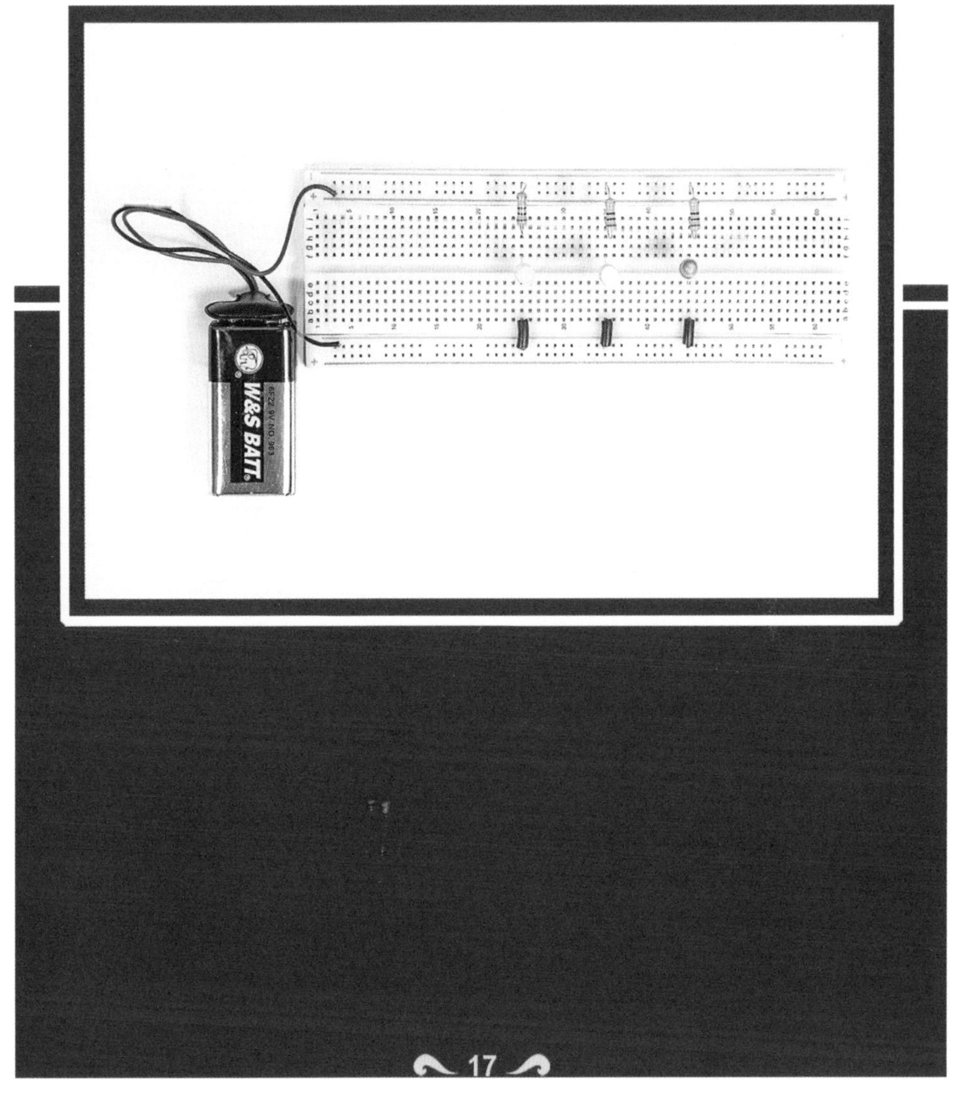

COMPONENTS

01
LED (Yellow,Green,Red)
3 nos.

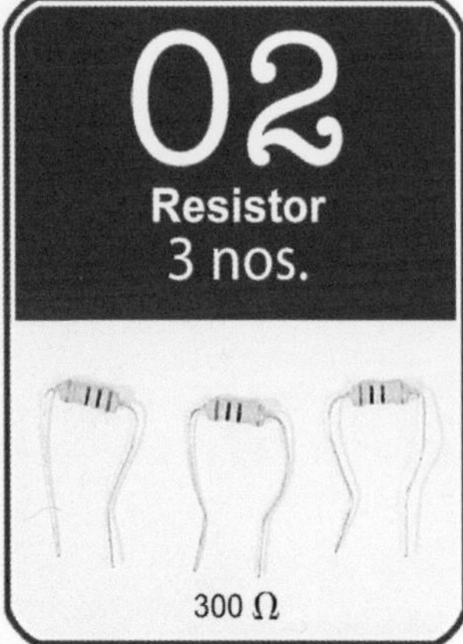
02
Resistor
3 nos.
300 Ω

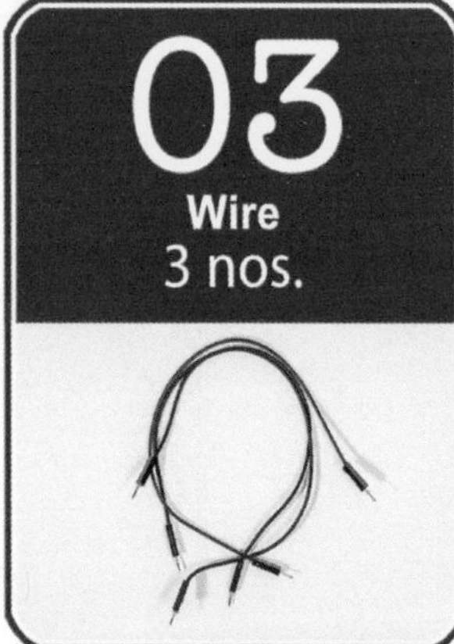
03
Wire
3 nos.

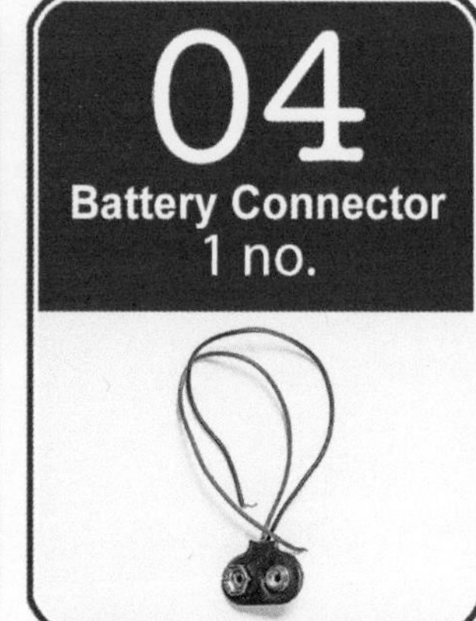
04
Battery Connector
1 no.

05
Battery 9V
1 no.
6F22 9V NO.963
W&S BATT

06
Breadboard
1 no.

Steps of Implementation

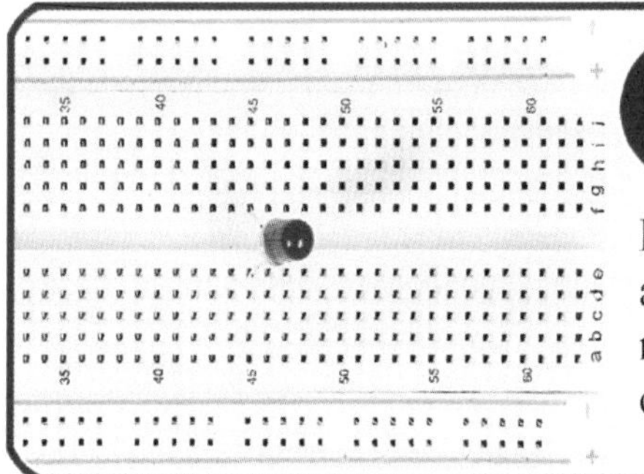

3.1

Put the positive pin of the red LED bulb at the meeting point of f and 45 and the negative pin of the red LED bulb into the convergence of e and 45.

3.2

Put the positive pin of the green LED bulb at the meeting point of f and 35 and the negative pin of the green LED bulb into the convergence of e and 35.

3.3

Put the positive pin of the yellow LED bulb at the meeting point of f and 25 and the negative pin of the yellow LED bulb into the convergence of e and 25.

3.4

Put one end of a 300 Ohm Resistor pin into the junction of j and 45 and the rest pin of it at the positive rail on the breadboard.

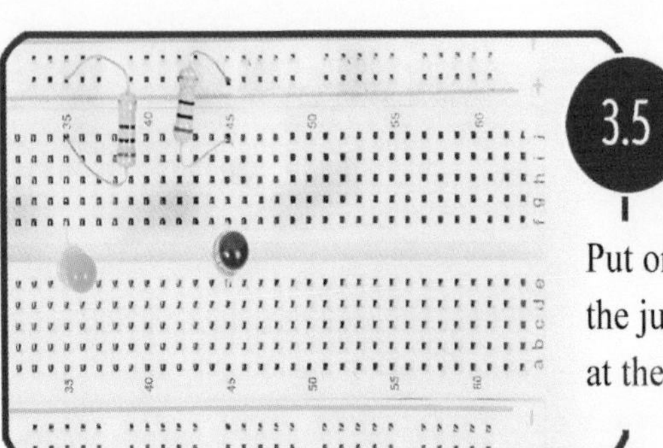

3.5

Put one end of a 300 Ohm Resistor pin into the junction of j and 35 and the rest pin of it at the positive rail on the breadboard.

3.6

Put one end of a 300 Ohm Resistor pin into the junction of j and 25 and the rest pin of it at the positive rail on the breadboard.

3.7

Insert one end of a wire into the meeting point of a and 45 and the other end into the negative rail on the breadboard.

3.8

Insert one end of a wire into the meeting point of a and 35 and the other end into the negative rail on the breadboard.

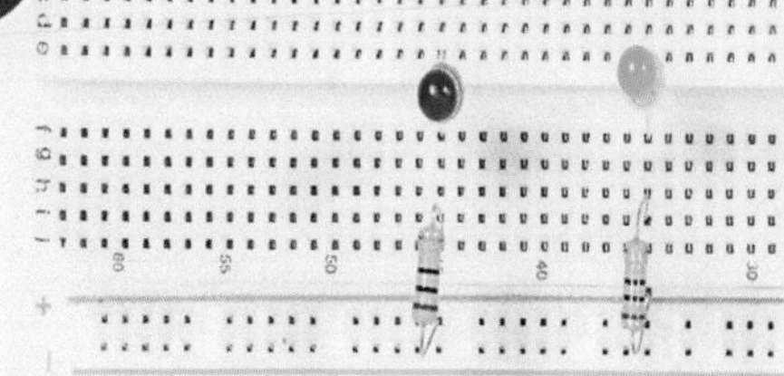

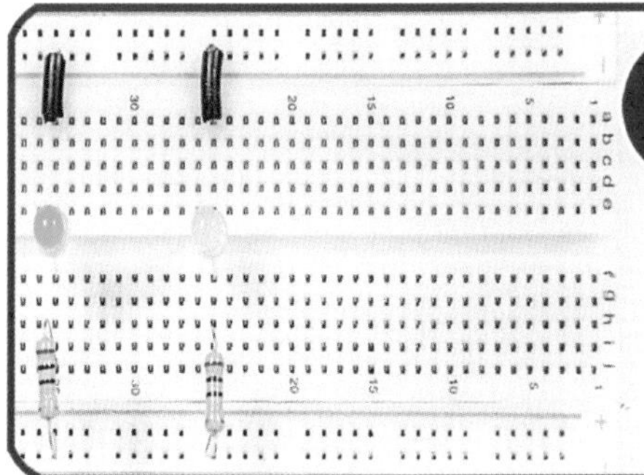

3.9

Insert one end of a wire into the meeting point of a and 25 and the other end into the negative rail on the breadboard.

3.10

Connect a 9V battery to the battery connector, and then connect the positive wire of the battery connector to the positive rail on the breadboard and the negative wire of the battery connector to the negative rail on the breadboard.

Figures 3.1 to 3.6 are the placement of components and Figures 3.7 to 3.10 are the figures of wiring the components. Three LED lights of different colors with a resistor respectively are connected in parallel to light up. Since they are connected in parallel, even if one LED lamp goes out, the rest of the lamps will continue to light up.

Parallel Circuit

A circuit in which the loads were linked in parallel is called a parallel circuit.
The supplied voltage across each load is the same, and the sum of all the currents flowing to each load equals the total current in the parallel circuit.

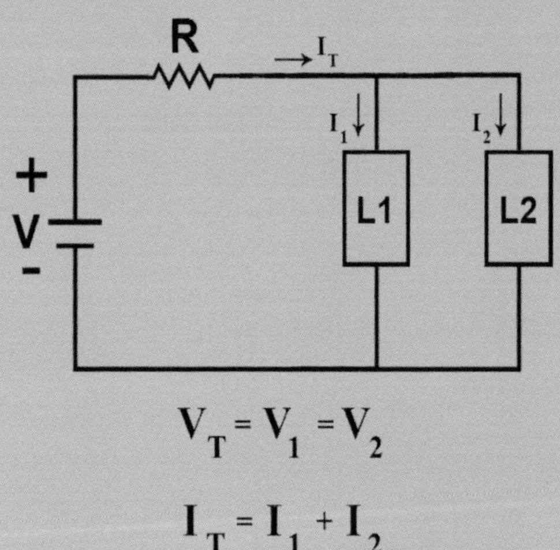

$$V_T = V_1 = V_2$$

$$I_T = I_1 + I_2$$

PROJECT (4)
Four LEDs connected in series and parallel circuit

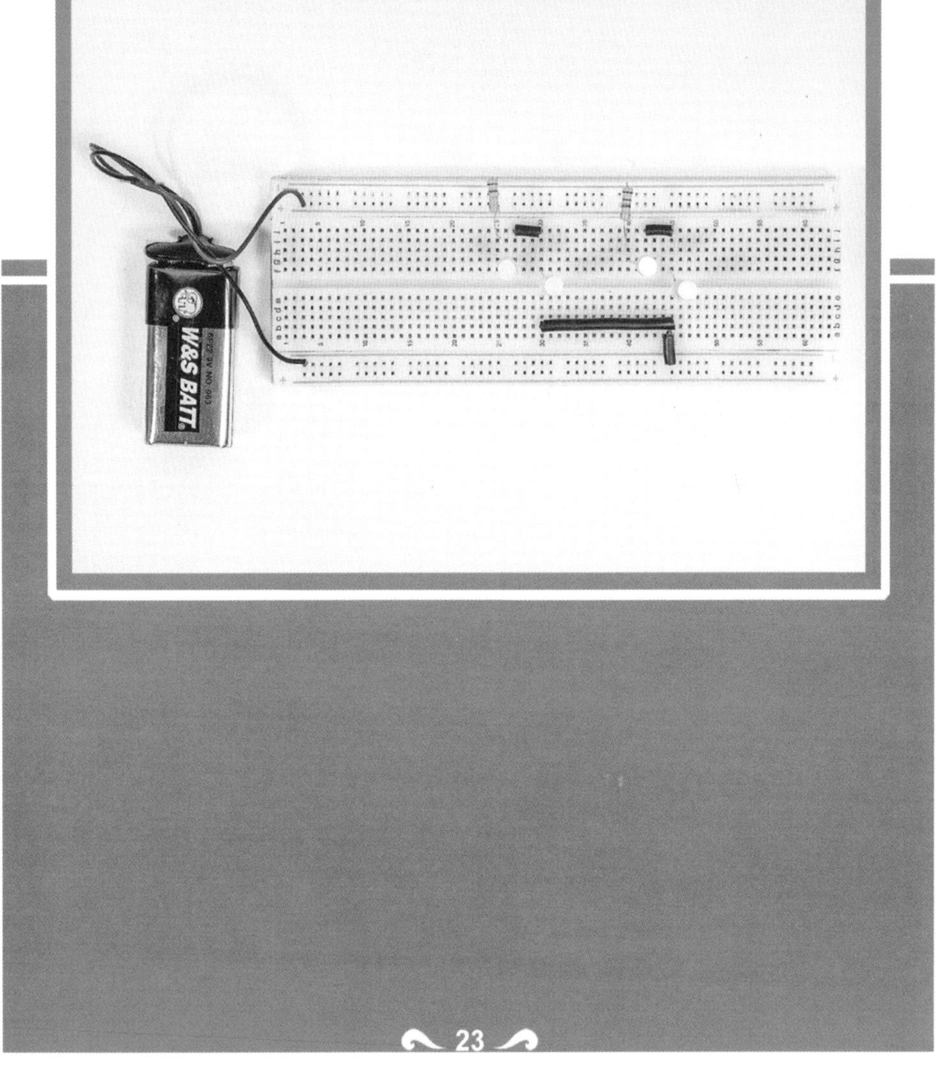

PROJECT (4)

COMPONENTS

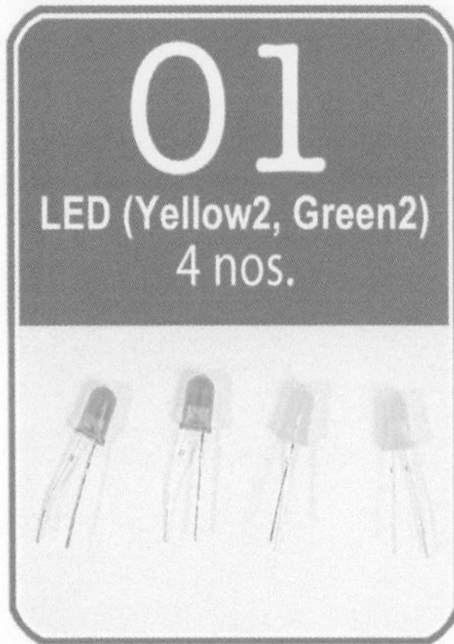

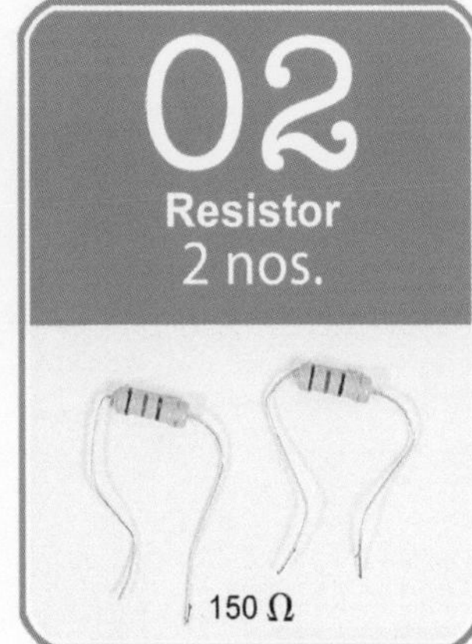

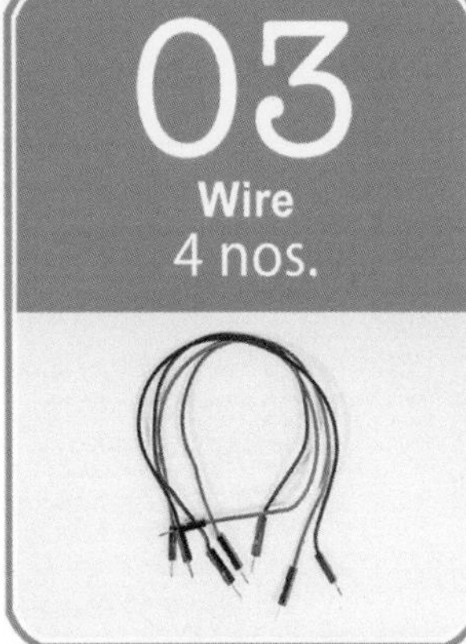

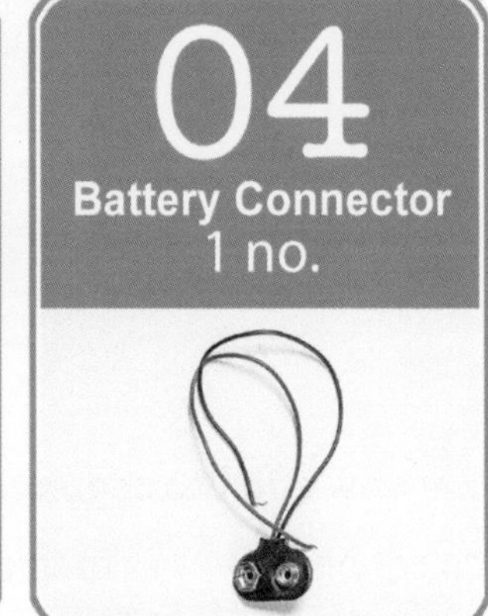

Steps of Implementation

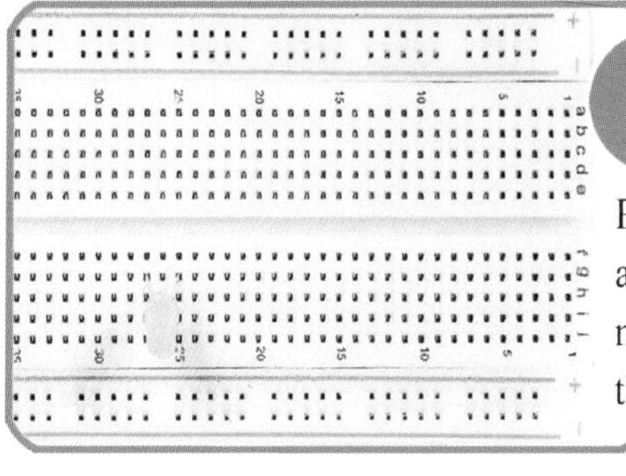

4.1

Put the positive pin of the yellow LED bulb at the meeting point of g and 25 and the negative pin of the yellow LED bulb into the convergence of g and 27.

4.2

Put the positive pin of the yellow LED bulb at the meeting point of f and 30 and the negative pin of the yellow LED bulb into the convergence of e and 30.

4.3

Put the positive pin of the green LED bulb at the meeting point of g and 40 and the negative pin of the green LED bulb into the convergence of g and 42.

4.4

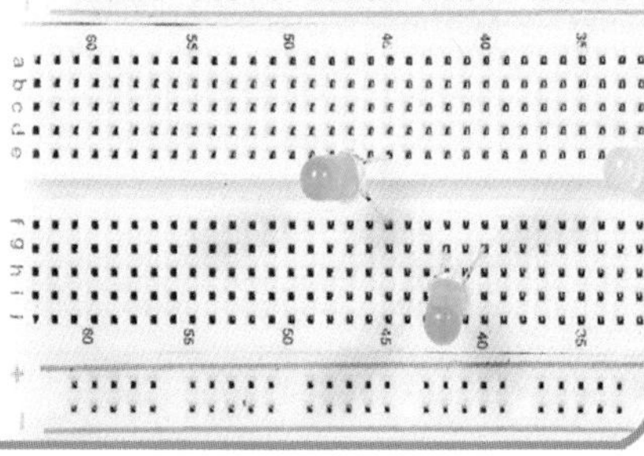

Put the positive pin of the green LED bulb at the meeting point of f and 45 and the negative pin of the green LED bulb into the convergence of e and 45.

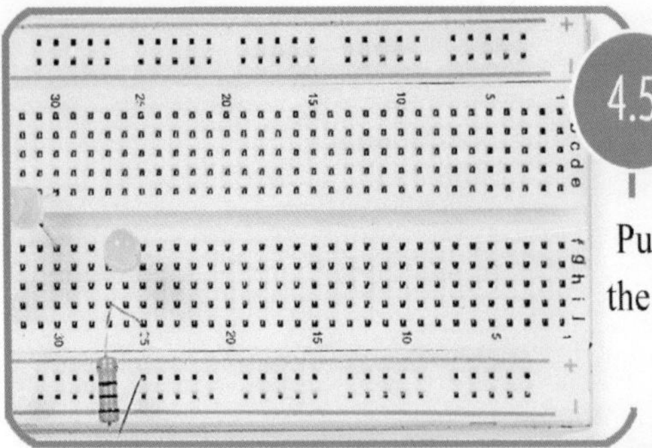

4.5

Put one end of a 150 Ohm Resistor pin into the junction of j and 25 and the rest pin of it at the positive rail on the breadboard.

4.6

Put one end of a 150 Ohm Resistor pin into the junction of j and 40 and the rest pin of it at the positive rail on the breadboard.

4.7

Insert one end of a wire into the meeting point of j and 27 and the other end into the meeting point of j and 30.

4.8

Insert one end of a wire into the meeting point of j and 42 and the other end into the meeting point of j and 45.

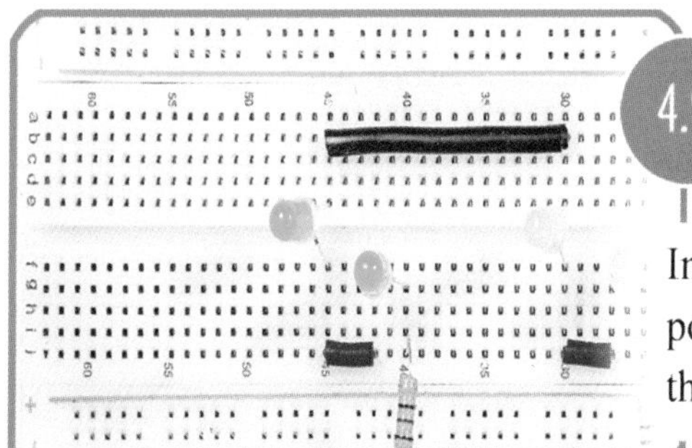

4.9

Insert one end of a wire into the meeting point of b and 30 and the other end into the meeting point of b and 45.

4.10

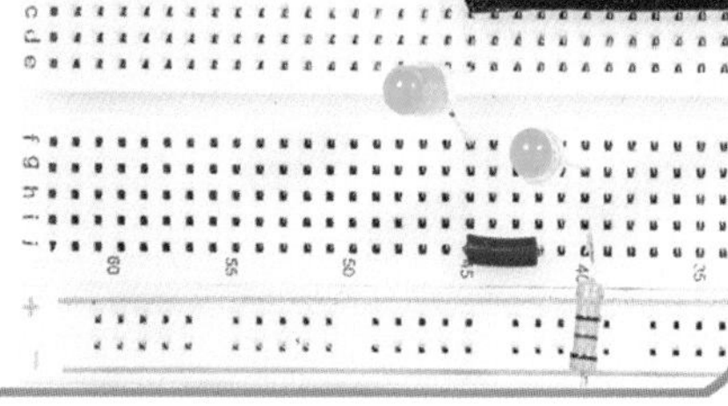

Insert one end of a wire into the meeting point of a and 45 and the other end into the negative rail on the breadboard.

4.11

Connect a 9V battery to the battery connector, and then connect the positive wire of the battery connector to the positive rail on the breadboard and the negative wire of the battery connector to the negative rail on the breadboard.

Explanation

Figures 4.1 to 4.5 are the placement of components and
Figures 4.7 to 4.11 are the figures of wiring the components.
The two yellow LEDs are connected in series,
and the two green LEDs are also connected in series.
These two sets of LEDs are connected in parallel with each resistor.
If one green LED is gone off, only the green
LED in series with it will be turn off,
and the two yellow LEDs will continue to light up.

PROJECT (5)
AUTOMATIC LIGHT AND DARK SENSOR

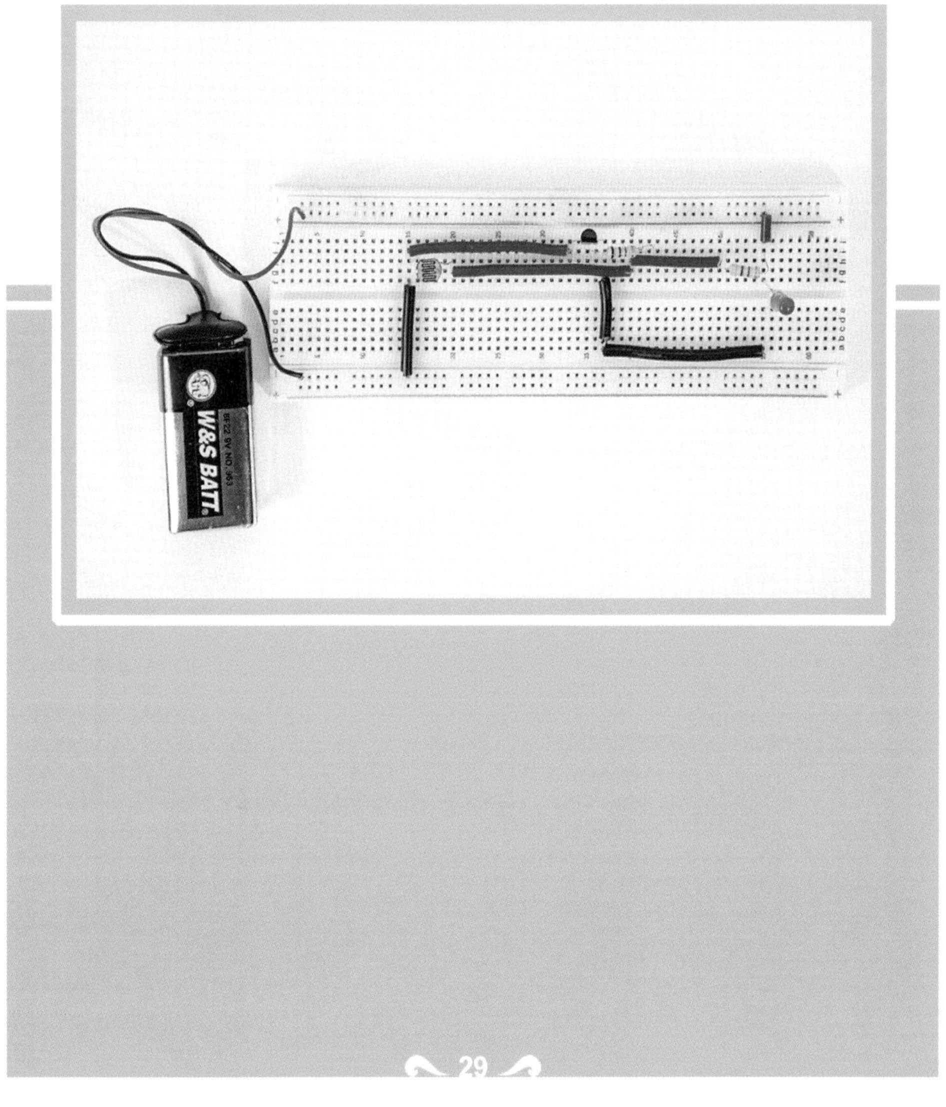

COMPONENTS

01
LED (Blue)
1 no.

02
Resistor
1 no.

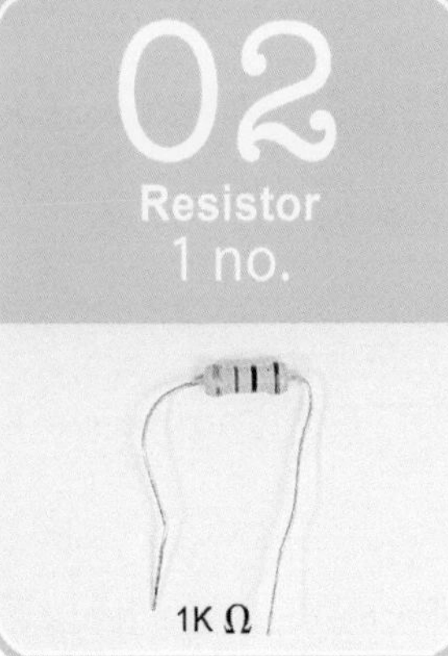

03
LDR
1 no.

04
Transistor BC 547
1 no.

05
Resistor
1 no.

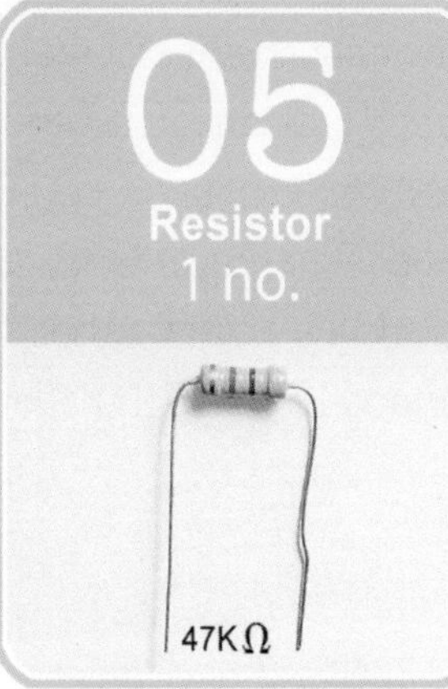

06
Wire
7 nos.

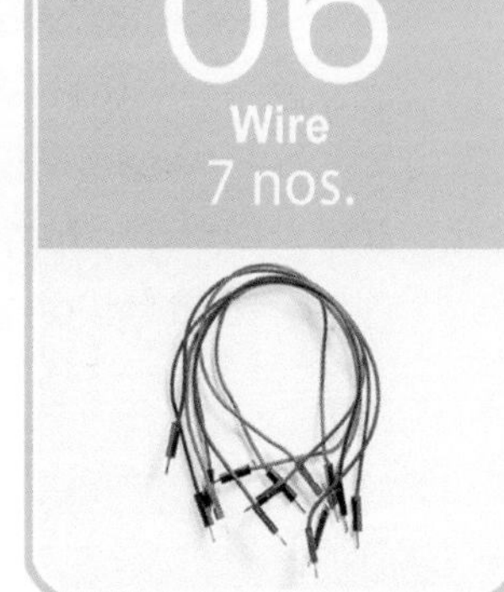

07
Battery Connector
1 no.

08
Battery 9V
1 no.

09
Breadboard
1 no.

Steps of Implementation

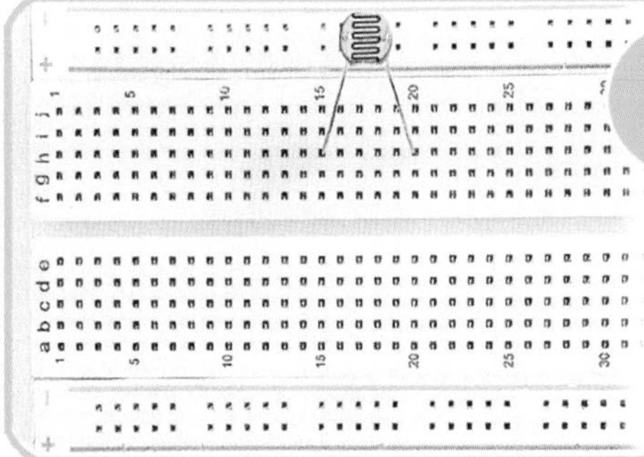

5.1

Insert one pin of an LDR where h meets 15 and the other pin of it at the meeting point of h and 20.

5.2

Place the collector pin of a transistor at the meeting point of j and 33 and the base pin of a transistor at the meeting point of j and 35, and the emitter pin of a transistor into the intersection of j and 37.

5.3

Put the positive pin of the blue LED bulb at the meeting point of f and 55 and the negative pin of the blue LED bulb into the convergence of e and 55.

5.4

Put one end of a 1K Ohm Resistor pin at the meeting point of i and 35 and the rest pin of it at the meeting point of i and 40.

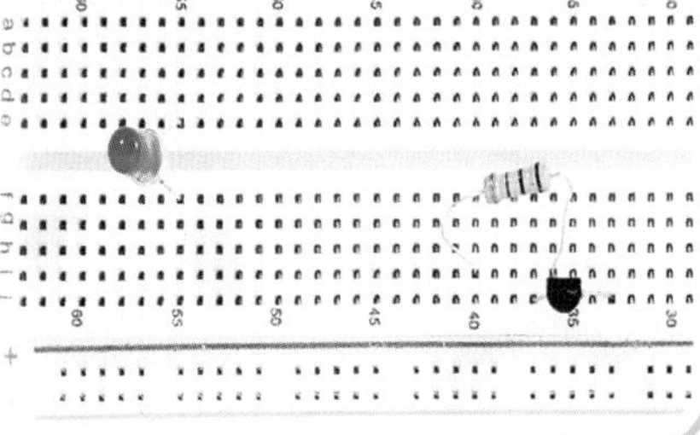

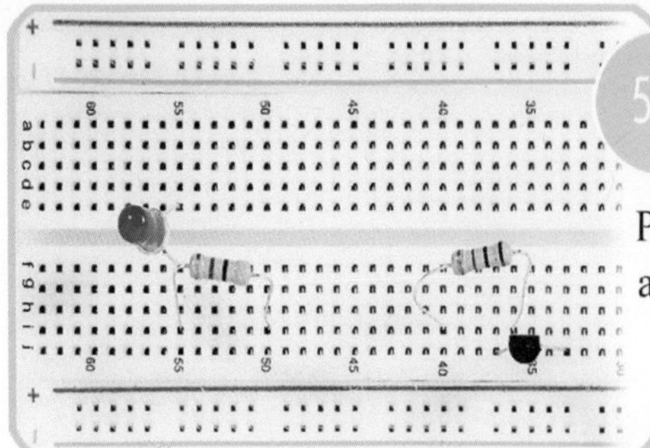

5.5

Put one end of a 47K Ohm Resistor pin at the meeting point of i and 50 and the rest pin of it at the meeting point of i and 55.

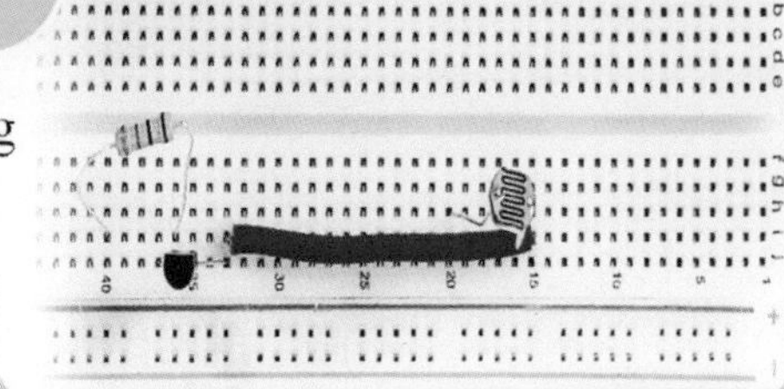

5.6

Insert one end of a wire into the meeting point of i and 15 and the other end into the meeting point of i and 33.

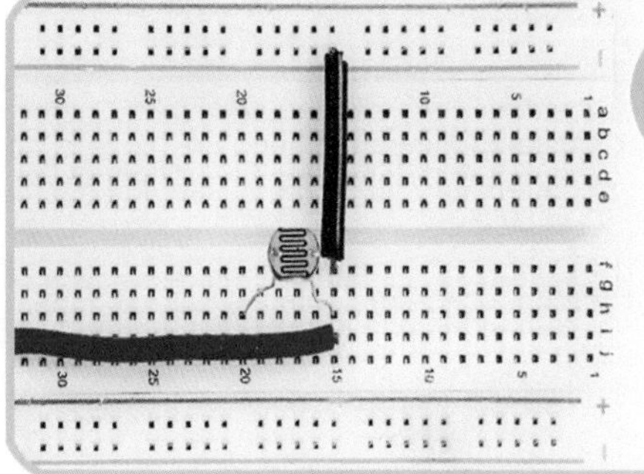

5.7

Insert one end of a wire into the meeting point of f and 15 and the other end into the negative rail on the breadboard.

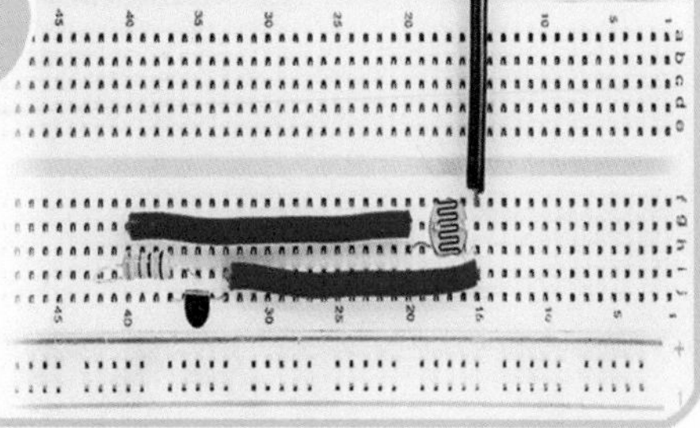

5.8

Insert one end of a wire into the meeting point of g and 20 and the other end into the meeting point of g and 40.

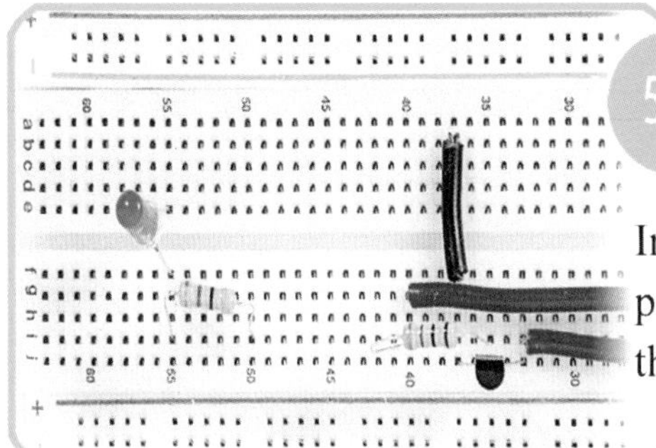

5.9

Insert one end of a wire into the meeting point of f and 37 and the other end into the meeting point of b and 37.

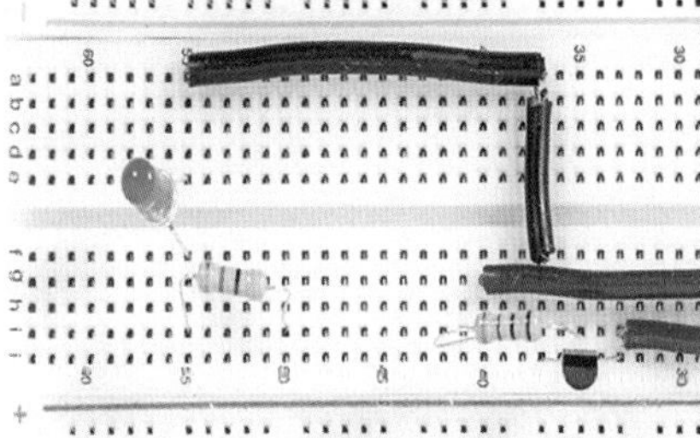

5.10

Insert one end of a wire into the meeting point of a and 37 and the other end into the meeting point of a and 55.

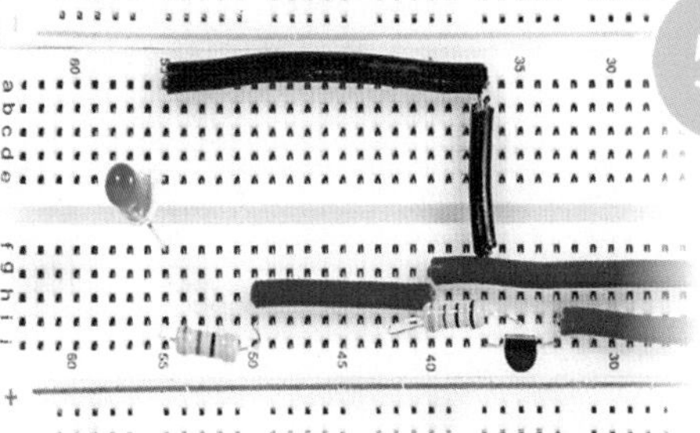

5.11

Insert one end of a wire into the meeting point of h and 40 and the other end into the meeting point of h and 50.

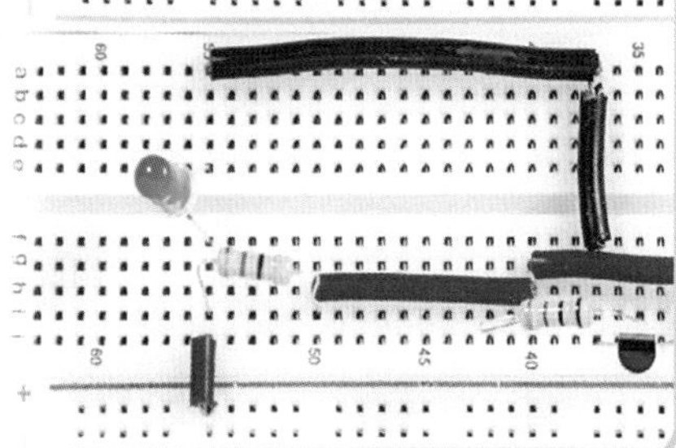

5.12

Insert one end of a wire into the meeting point of j and 55 and the other end into the positive rail on the breadboard.

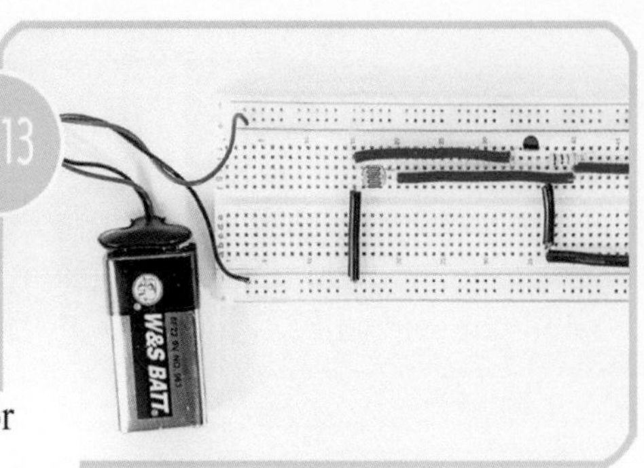

Connect a 9V battery to the battery connector, and then connect the positive wire of the battery connector to the positive rail on the breadboard and the negative wire of the battery connector to the negative rail on the breadboard.

Explanation

Figures 5.1 to 5.5 are the placement of components and Figures 5.6 to 5.13 are the figures of wiring the components.
If light falls on an LDR,
the LED will turn off.
When no light falls on the LDR, the LED will light up.
The LDR is connected to the collector of a transistor and
The LED is connected to the side of the emitter of the transistor.

PROJECT (6)
A BLINKING LEDs CIRCUIT

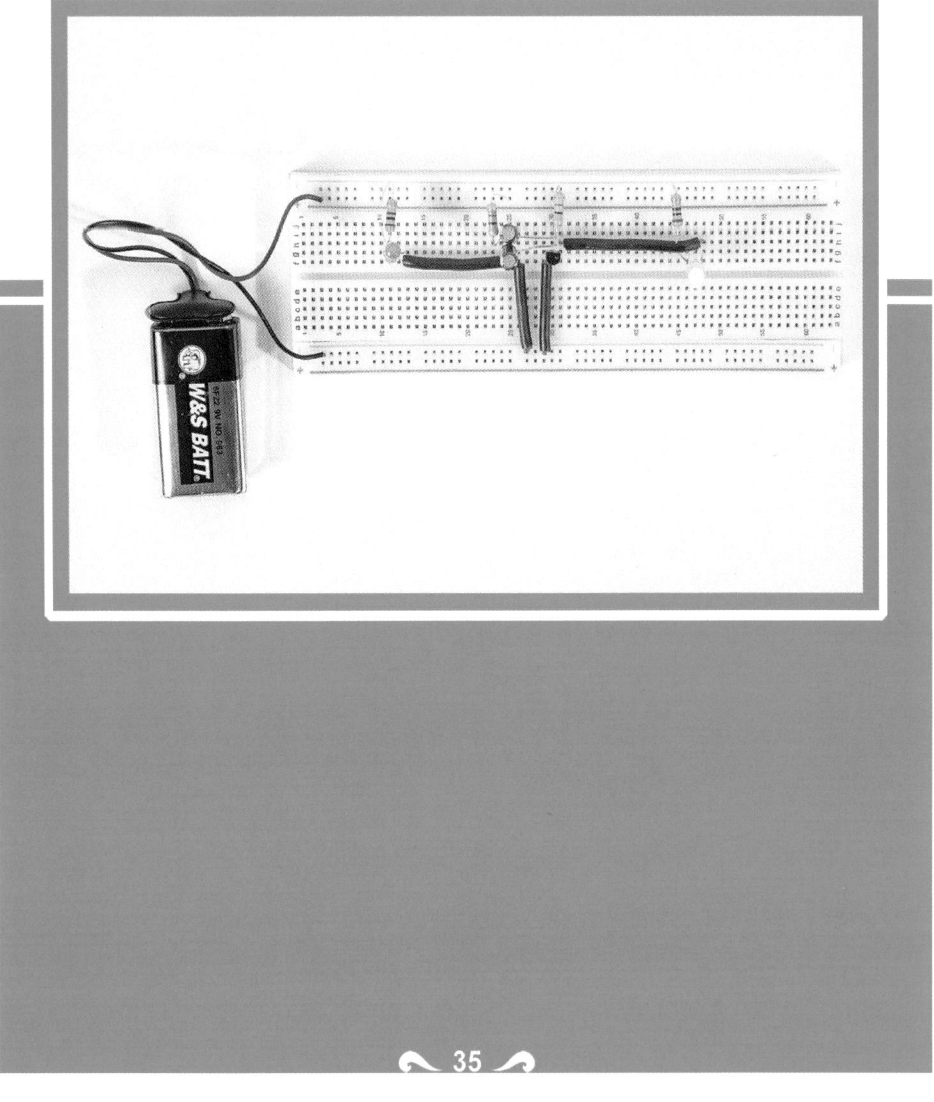

COMPONENTS

01
LED (Blue 1 , Yellow 1)
2 nos.

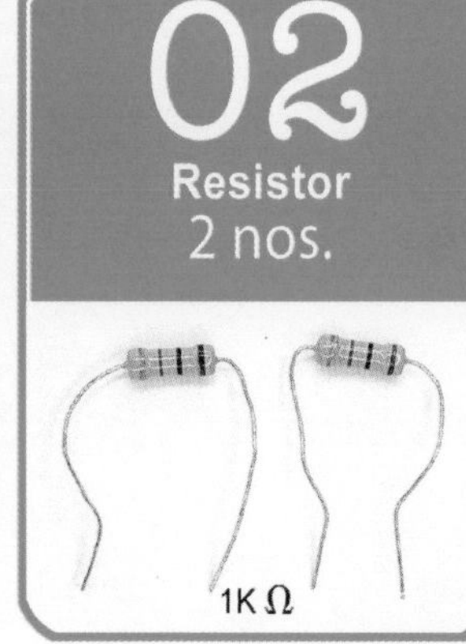

02
Resistor
2 nos.

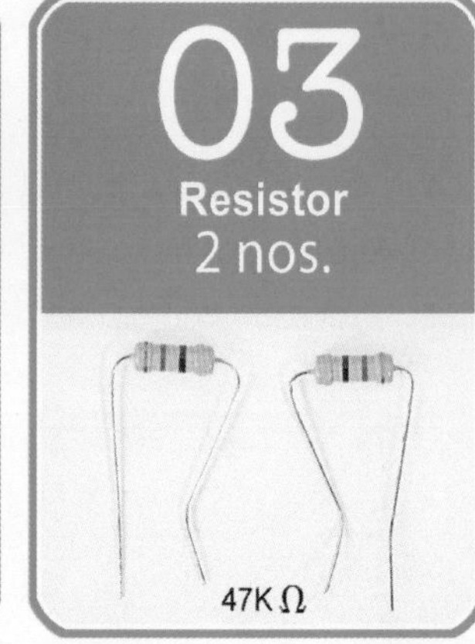

03
Resistor
2 nos.

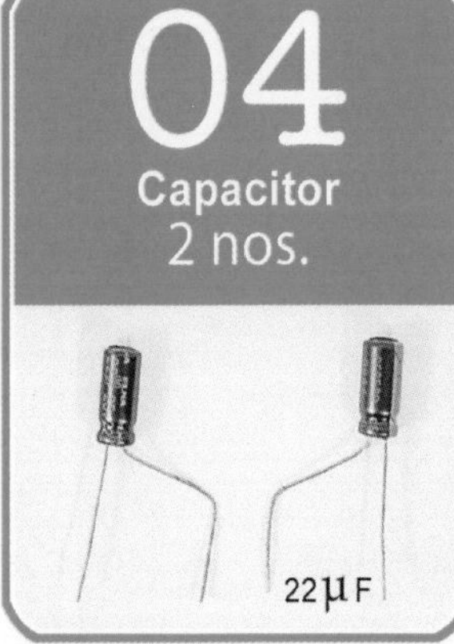

04
Capacitor
2 nos.

05
Transistor BC 547
2 nos.

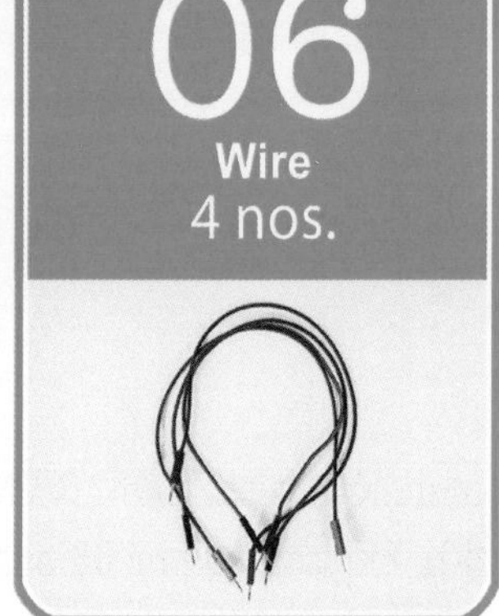

06
Wire
4 nos.

07
Battery Connector
1 no.

08
Battery 9V
1 no.

09
Breadboard
1 no.

Steps of Implementation

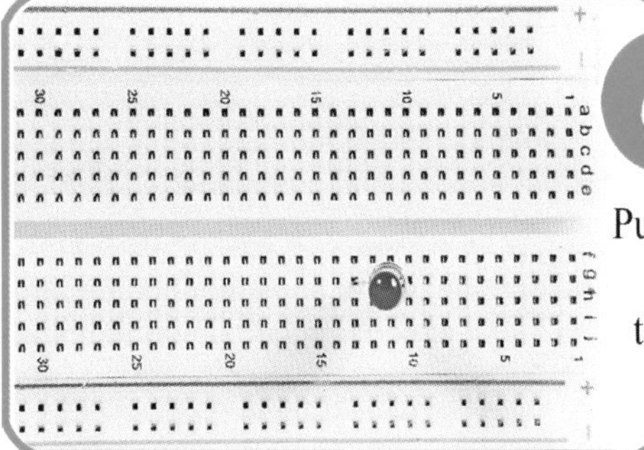

6.1

Put the positive pin of the blue LED bulb at the meeting point of g and 10 and the negative pin of the blue LED bulb into the convergence of g and 13.

6.2

Put the positive pin of the yellow LED bulb at the meeting point of g and 45 and the negative pin of the yellow LED bulb into the convergence of g and 48.

6.3

Place the collector pin of a transistor at the meeting point of g and 24 and the base pin of a transistor at the meeting point of g and 25, and the emitter pin of a transistor into the intersection of g and 26.

6.4

Place the collector pin of a transistor at the meeting point of g and 31 and
the base pin of a transistor at the meeting point of g and 30,
and the emitter pin of a transistor into the intersection of g and 29.

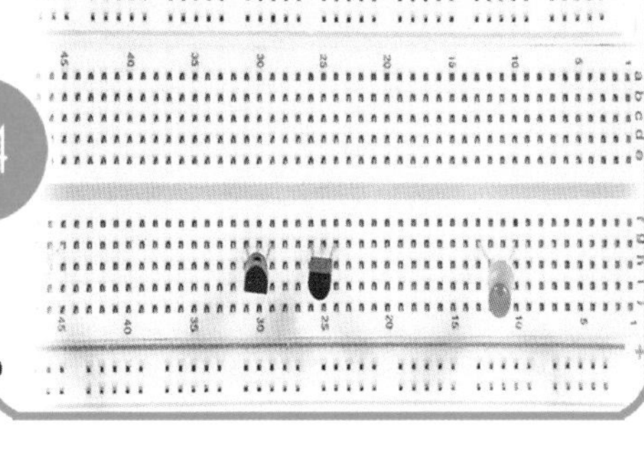

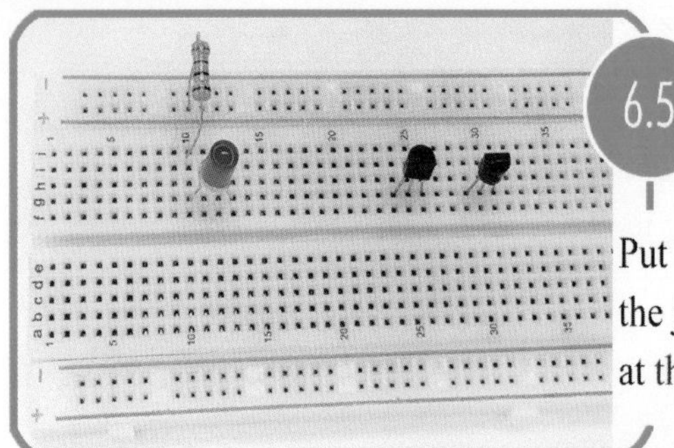

6.5

Put one end of a 1K Ohm Resistor pin into the junction of j and 10 and the rest pin of it at the positive rail on the breadboard.

6.6

Put one end of a 47K Ohm Resistor pin into the junction of j and 25 and the rest pin of it at the positive rail on the breadboard.

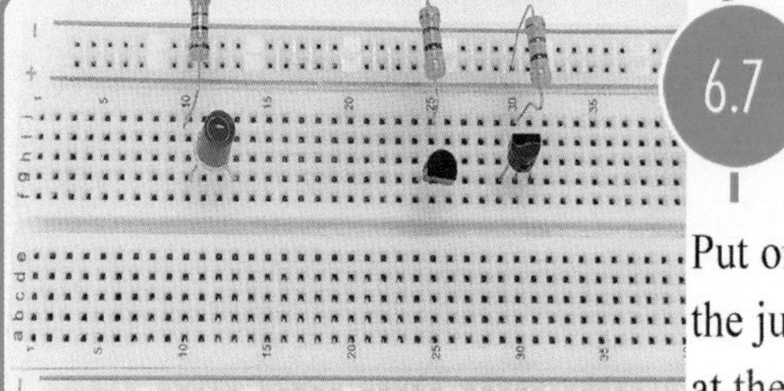

6.7

Put one end of a 47K Ohm Resistor pin into the junction of j and 30 and the rest pin of it at the positive rail on the breadboard.

6.8

Put one end of a 1K Ohm Resistor pin into the junction of j and 45 and the rest pin of it at the positive rail on the breadboard.

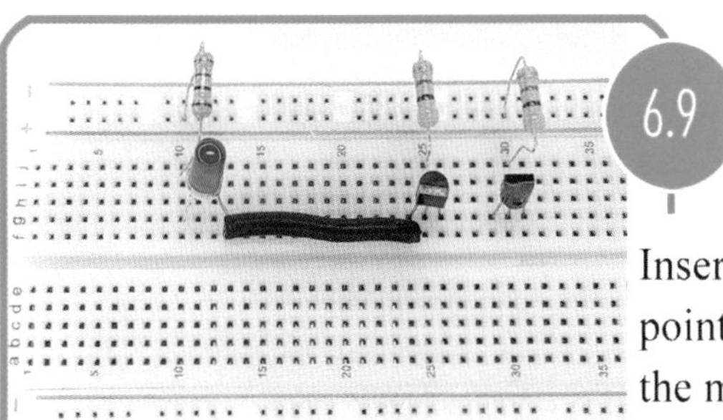

6.9

Insert one end of a wire into the meeting point of f and 13 and the other end into the meeting point of f and 24.

6.10

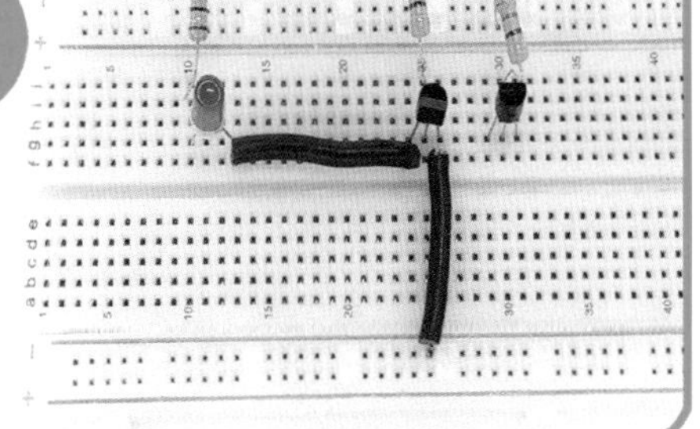

Insert one end of a wire into the meeting point of f and 26 and the other end into the negative rail on the breadboard.

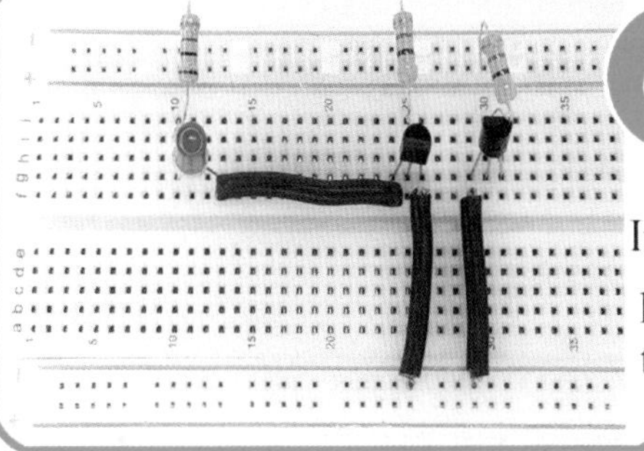

6.11

Insert one end of a wire into the meeting point of f and 29 and the other end into the negative rail on the breadboard.

6.12

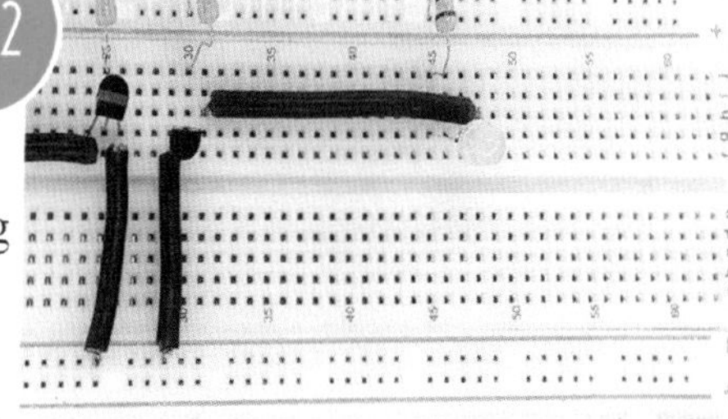

Insert one end of a wire into the meeting point of h and 31 and the other end into the meeting point of h and 48.

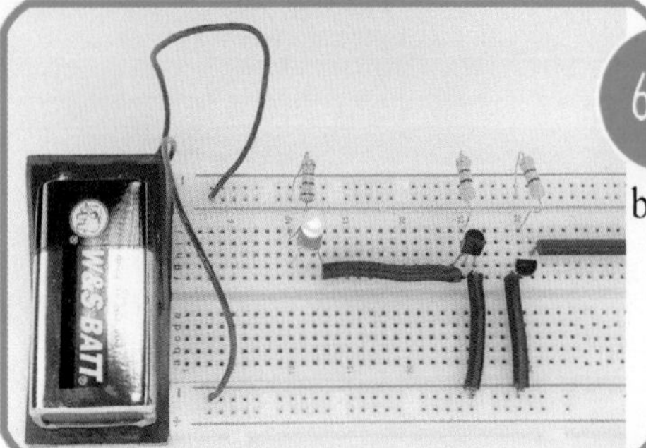

6.13

Connect a 9V battery to the battery connector, and then connect the positive wire of the battery connector to the positive rail on the breadboard and the negative wire of the battery connector to the negative rail on the breadboard.

6.14

Put one pin of a capacitor at the meeting point of h and 24 and the other pin of it at the meeting point of h and 30.

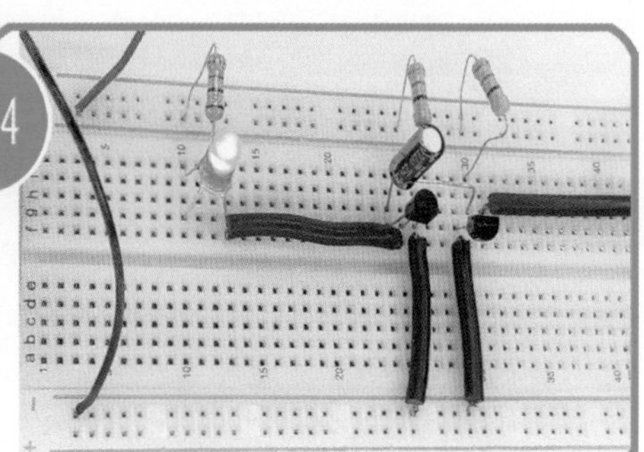

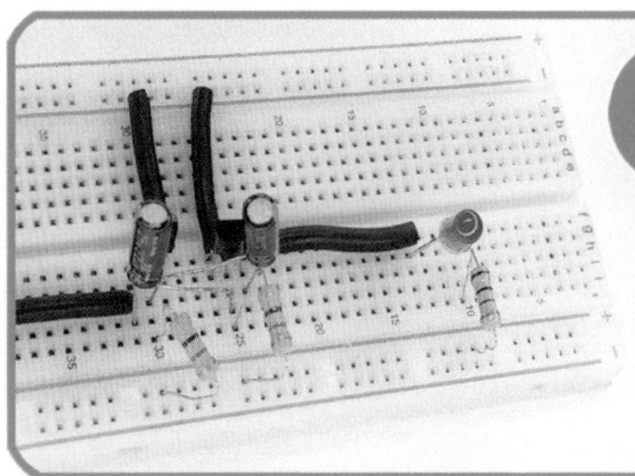

6.15

Put one pin of a capacitor at the meeting point of i and 25 and the other pin of it at the meeting point of i and 31.

Explanation

Figures 6.1 to 6.8 are the placement of components and Figures 6.9 to 6.13 are the figures of wiring the components. Based on the method of making one LED light up with one transistor, two LEDs are made light up simultaneously by using two transistors connected with a resistor. Figures 6.14 to 6.15 show two transistors are connected to two capacitors to make the LEDs blinking.

PROJECT (7)
A LASER SECURITY LAMP

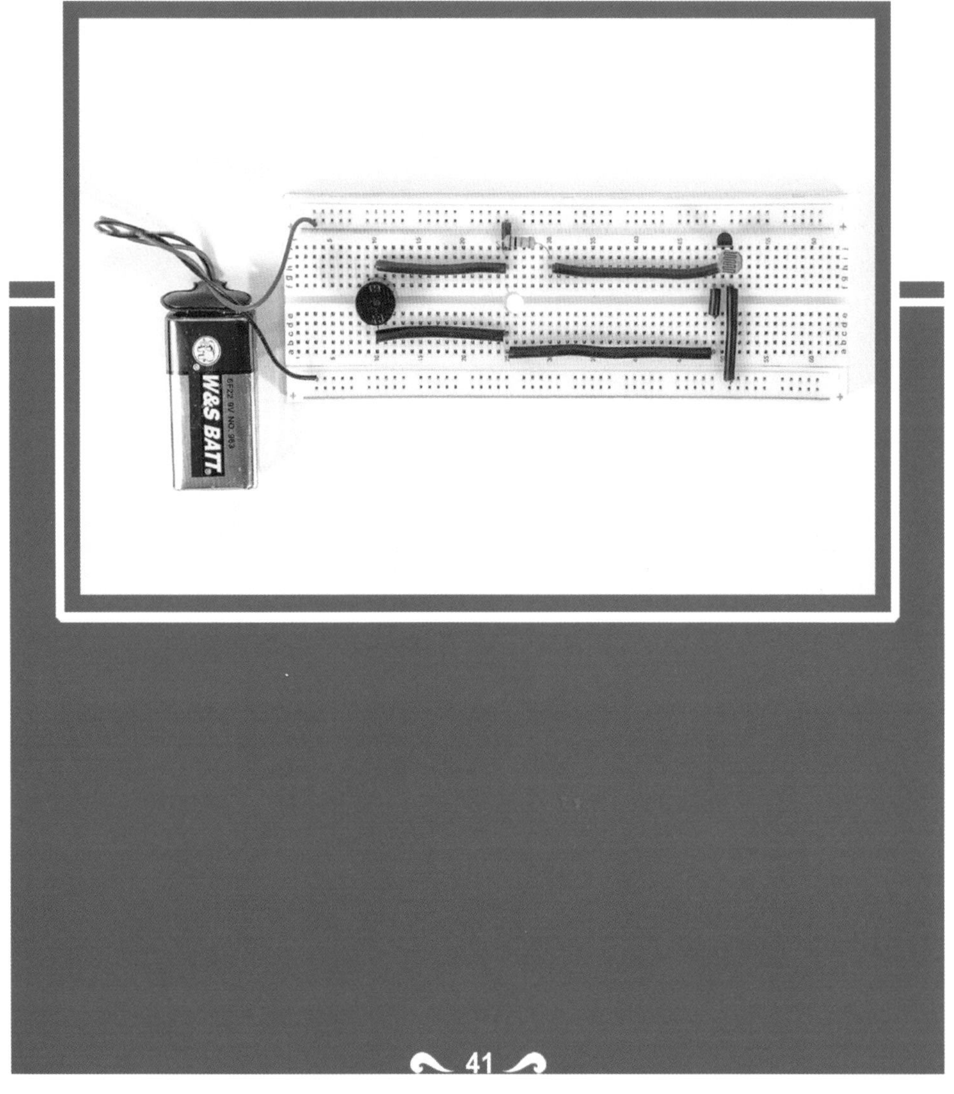

COMPONENTS

01
LED (Green)
1 no.

02
Resistor
1 no.

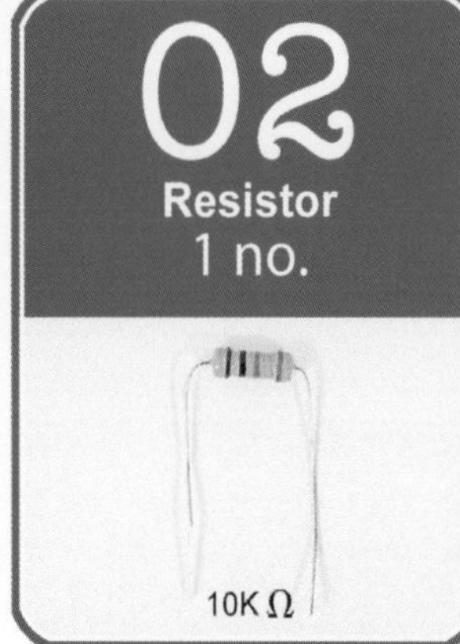

03
LDR
1 no.

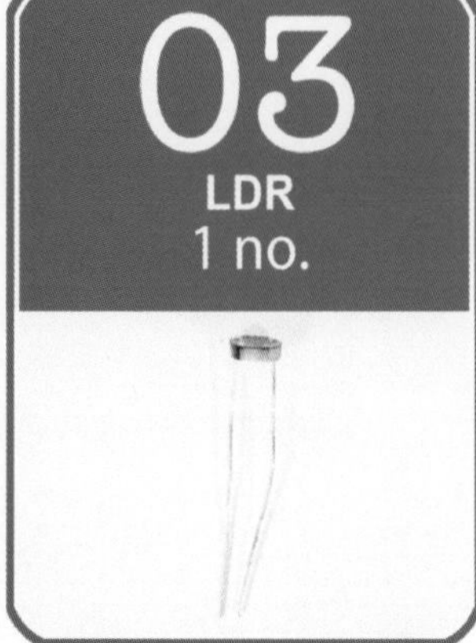

04
DC Buzzer
1 no.

05
Transistor 2N2222A
1 no.

06
Wire
7 nos.

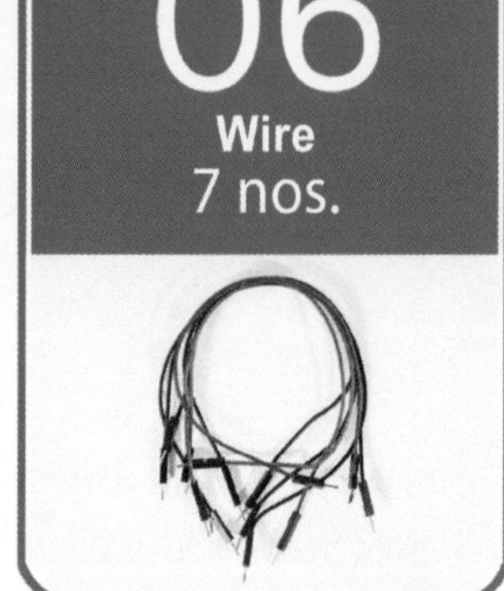

07
Battery Connector
1 no.

08
Battery 9V
1 no.

09
Breadboard
1 no.

Steps of Implementation

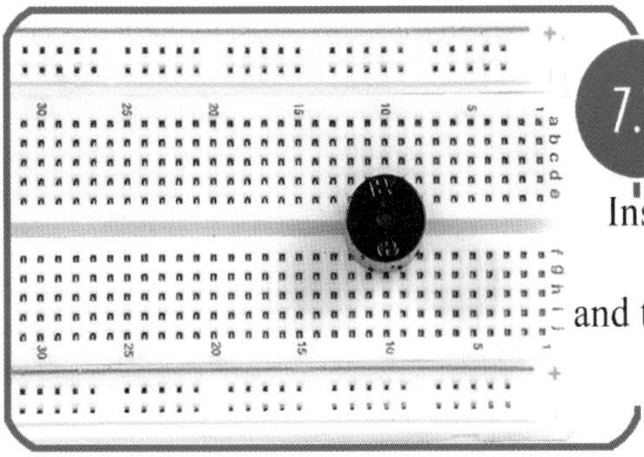

7.1

Insert the positive pin of a DC Buzzer into the meeting point of f and 10 and the negative pin at the meeting point of e and 10.

7.2

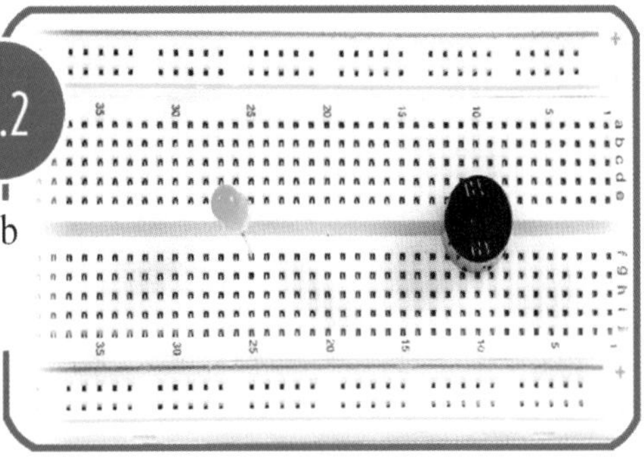

Put the positive pin of the green LED bulb at the meeting point of f and 25 and the negative pin of the green LED bulb into the convergence of e and 20.

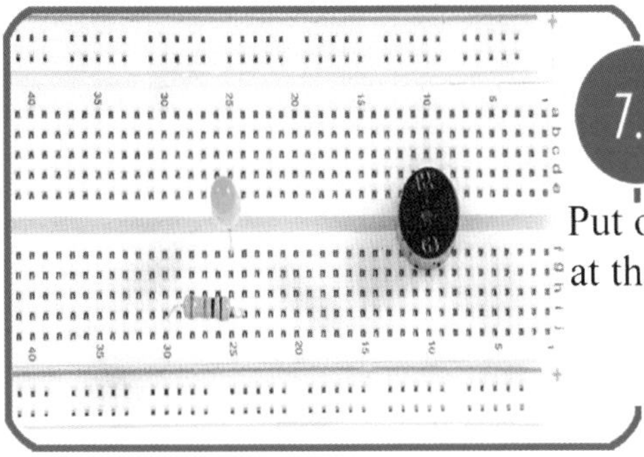

7.3

Put one end of a 10K Ohm Resistor pin at the meeting point of i and 25 and the rest pin of it at the meeting point of i and 30.

7.4

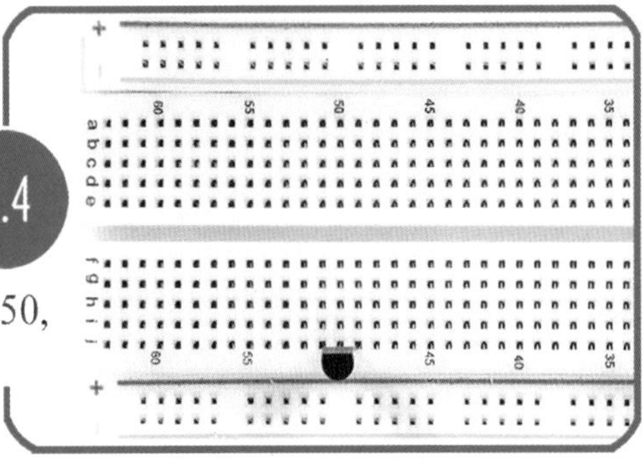

Place the collector pin of a transistor at the meeting point of j and 49 and the base pin of a transistor at the meeting point of j and 50, and the emitter pin of a transistor into the intersection of j and 51.

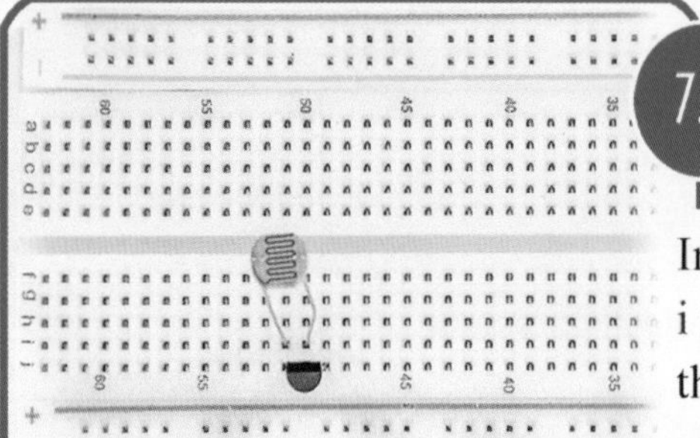

7.5

Insert one pin of an LDR where i meets 50 and the other pin of it at the meeting point of i and 51.

7.6

Insert one end of a wire into the meeting point of h and 10 and the other end into the meeting point of h and 25.

7.7

Insert one end of a wire into the meeting point of c and 10 and the other end into the meeting point of c and 25.

7.8

Insert one end of a wire into the meeting point of j and 25 and the other end into the positive rail on the breadboard.

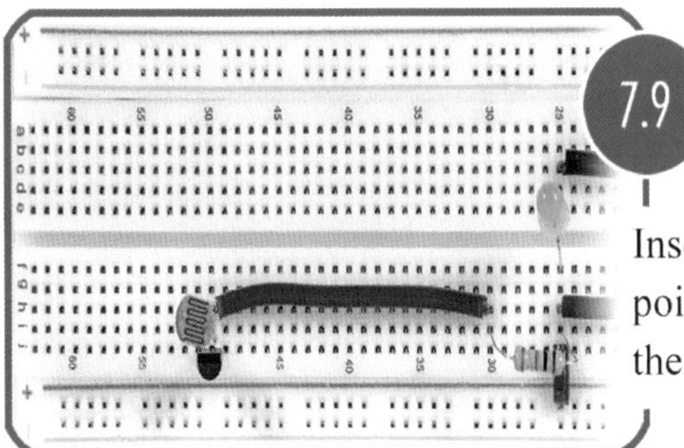

7.9

Insert one end of a wire into the meeting point of h and 30 and the other end into the meeting point of h and 50.

7.10

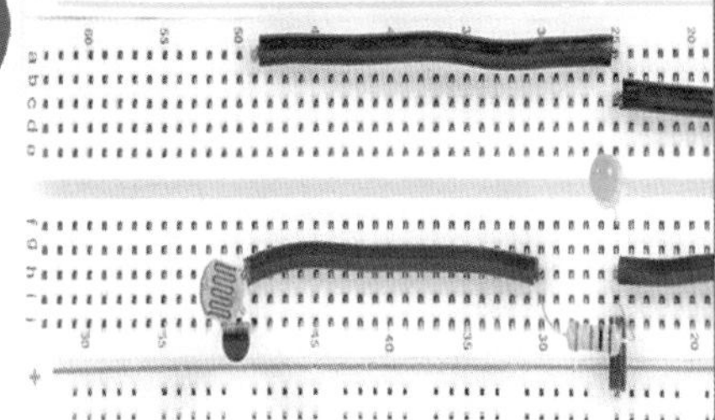

Insert one end of a wire into the meeting point of a and 25 and the other end into the meeting point of a and 49.

7.11

Insert one end of a wire into the meeting point of f and 49 and the other end into the meeting point of e and 49.

7.12

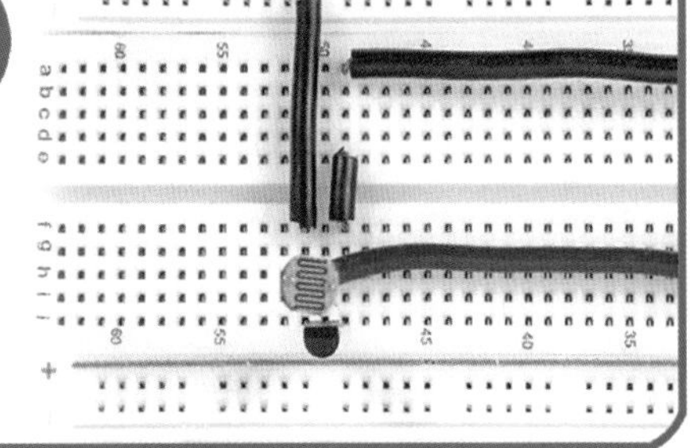

Insert one end of a wire into the meeting point of f and 51 and the other end into the negative rail on the breadboard.

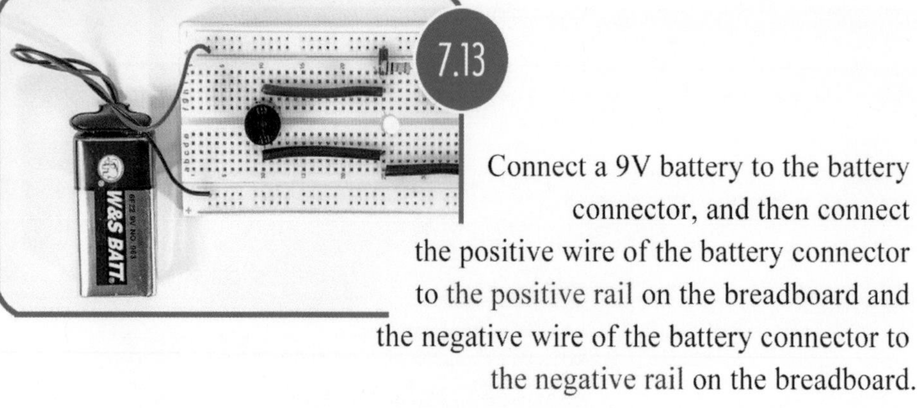

Connect a 9V battery to the battery connector, and then connect the positive wire of the battery connector to the positive rail on the breadboard and the negative wire of the battery connector to the negative rail on the breadboard.

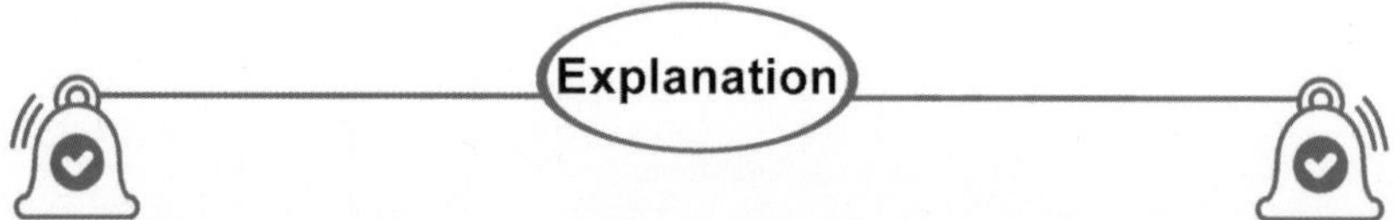

Figures 7.1 to 7.5 are the placement of components and Figures 7.6 to 7.13 are the figures of wiring the components.
It is to make a laser light onto the LDR.
If any shadow passes between the LDR and the laser light, the buzzer will sound, and the LED will light up.
DC buzzer and LED light are connected in series and connected to the collector of a transistor, and LDR is connected to the side of the emitter of it.

PROJECT (8)
A DOOR BELL

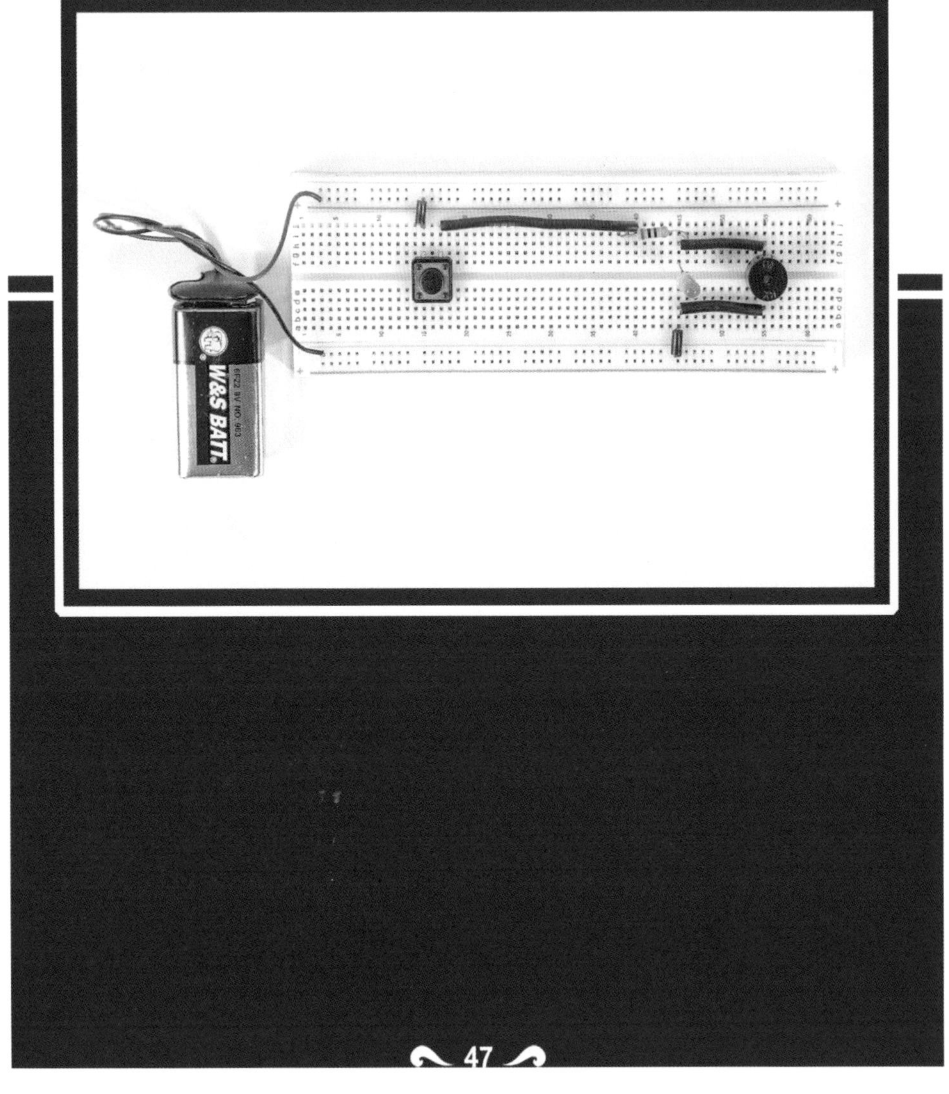

COMPONENTS

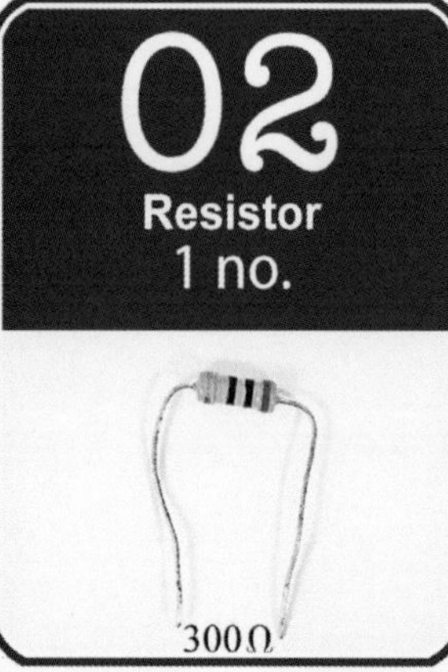

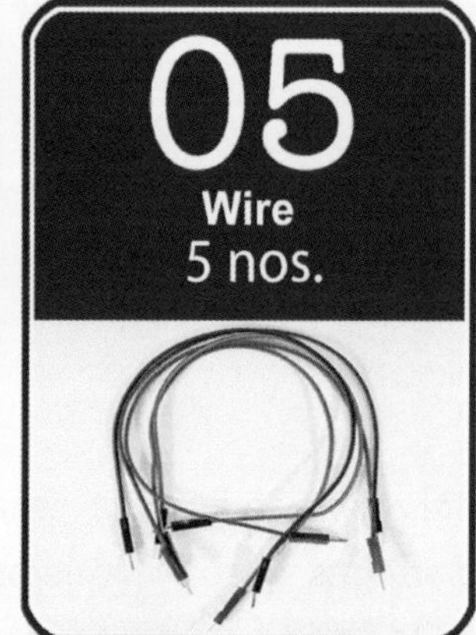

08
Breadboard
1 no.

Steps of Implementation

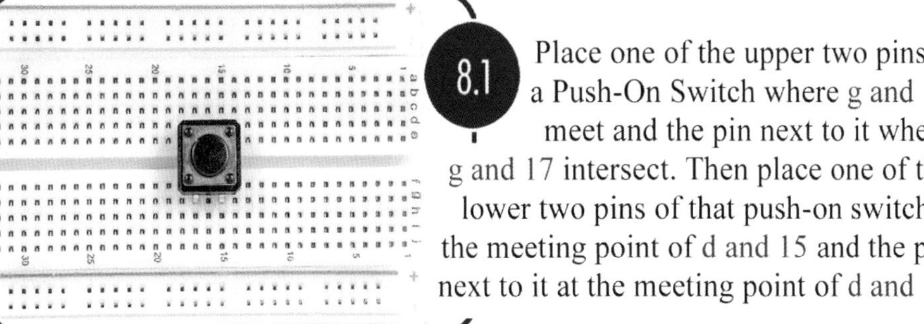

8.1 Place one of the upper two pins of a Push-On Switch where g and 15 meet and the pin next to it where g and 17 intersect. Then place one of the lower two pins of that push-on switch at the meeting point of d and 15 and the pin next to it at the meeting point of d and 17.

8.2 Put the positive pin of the blue LED bulb at the meeting point of f and 45 and the negative pin of the blue LED bulb into the convergence of e and 45.

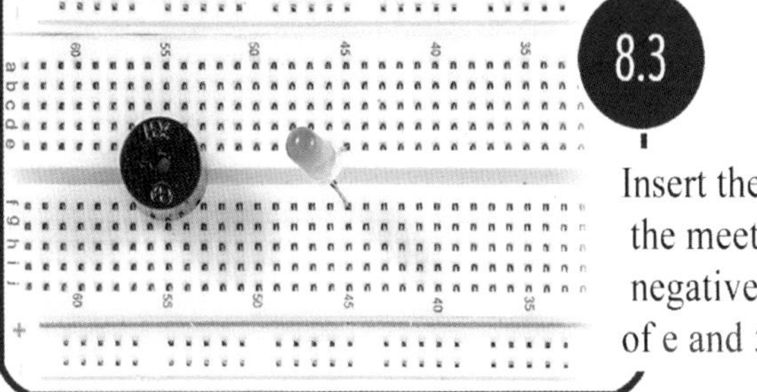

8.3 Insert the positive pin of a DC Buzzer into the meeting point of f and 55 and the negative pin at the meeting point of e and 55.

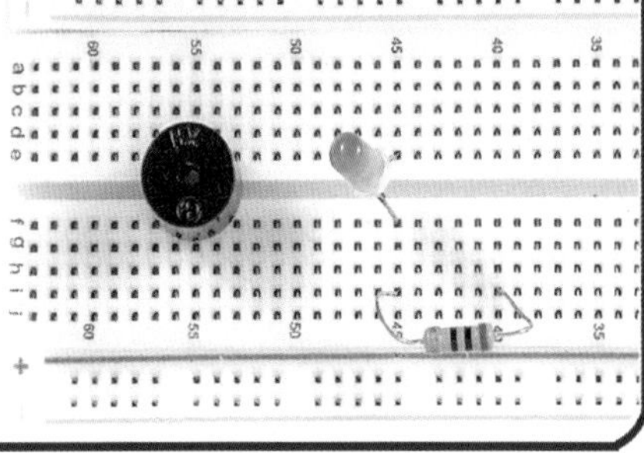

8.4 Put one end of a 300 Ohm Resistor pin at the meeting point of i and 40 and the rest pin of it at the meeting point of i and 45.

8.5

Insert one end of a wire into the meeting point of j and 15 and the other end into the positive rail on the breadboard.

8.6

Insert one end of a wire into the meeting point of j and 17 and the other end into the meeting point of j and 40.

8.7

Insert one end of a wire into the meeting point of h and 45 and the other end into the meeting point of h and 55.

8.8

Insert one end of a wire into the meeting point of c and 45 and the other end into the meeting point of c and 55.

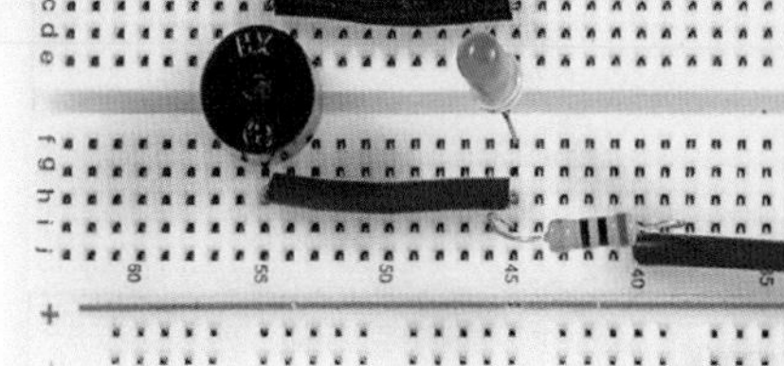

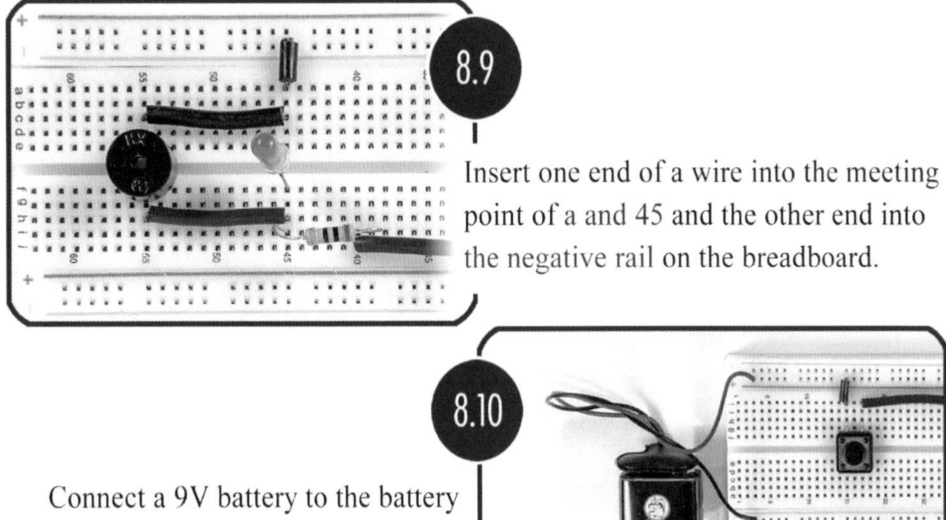

Insert one end of a wire into the meeting point of a and 45 and the other end into the negative rail on the breadboard.

Connect a 9V battery to the battery connector, and then connect the positive wire of the battery connector to the positive rail on the breadboard and the negative wire of the battery connector to the negative rail on the breadboard.

Figures 8.1 to 8.4 are the placement of components and Figures 8.5 to 8.10 are the figures of wiring the components. When pressing the push button, the LED bulb will light up, and the buzzer will sound. When releasing the Push Button, the light will turn off, and the sound will stop. LED bulb and DC Buzzer are connected in series.

Resistor Color Code

Carbon-Composition Resistors are color-coded on their body to comfortably identify their resistance value.

Color	Value	Tolerance
Black	0	
Brown	1	± 1%
Red	2	± 2%
Orange	3	
Yellow	4	
Green	5	
Blue	6	
Violet	7	
Grey	8	
White	9	
Gold		± 5%
Silver		±10%

There are four-color bands, five-color bands, six-color bands, and so on. Let's study how to read the four-color band resistor.

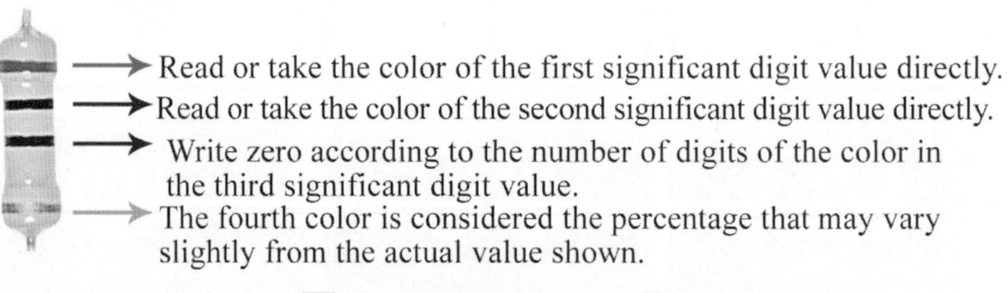

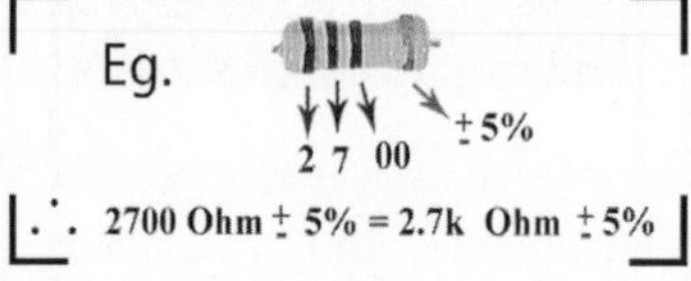

Note. Since the value of the black color is zero, take only the two color digit values from the first and second place, if it is in the third significant digit value.

PROJECT (9)
A Water Level Indicator

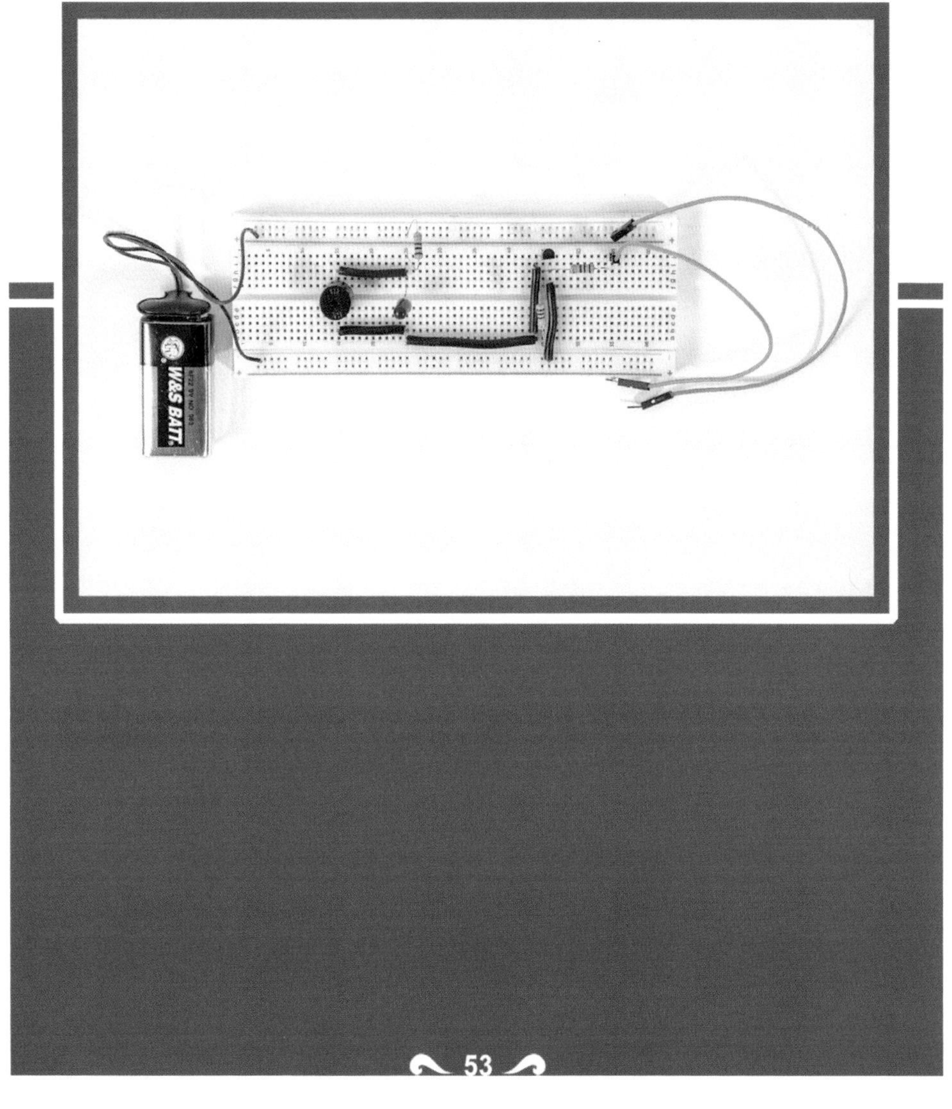

COMPONENTS

01
LED (Red)
1 no.

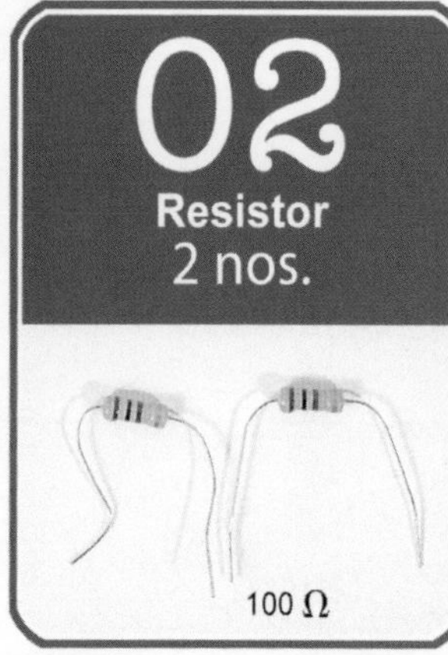
02
Resistor
2 nos.
100 Ω

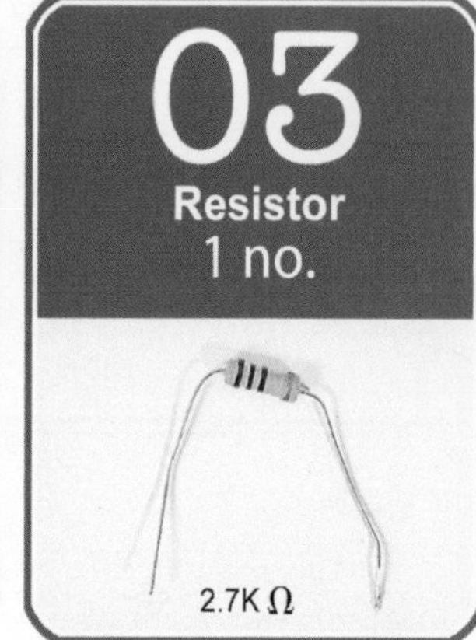
03
Resistor
1 no.
2.7K Ω

04
DC Buzzer
1 no.

05
Transistor BC 547
1 no.

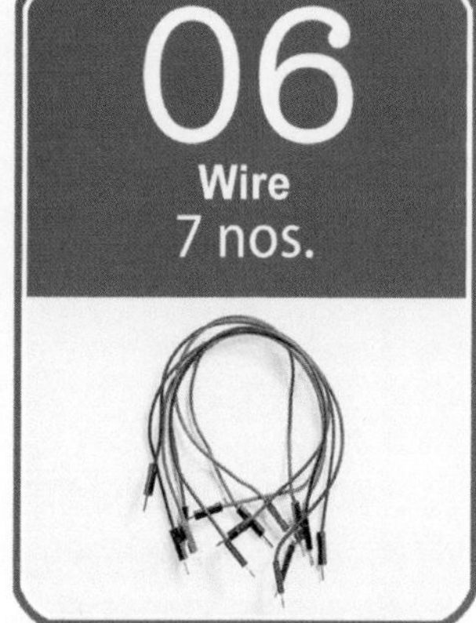
06
Wire
7 nos.

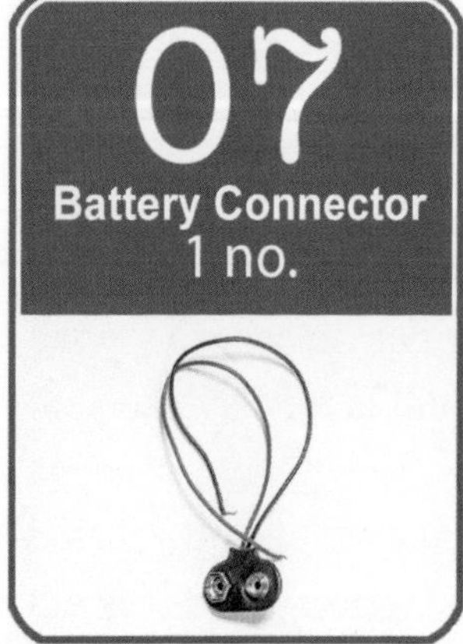
07
Battery Connector
1 no.

08
Battery 9V
1 no.
6F22 9V NO. 963
W&S BATT.

09
Breadboard
1 no.

Steps of Implementation

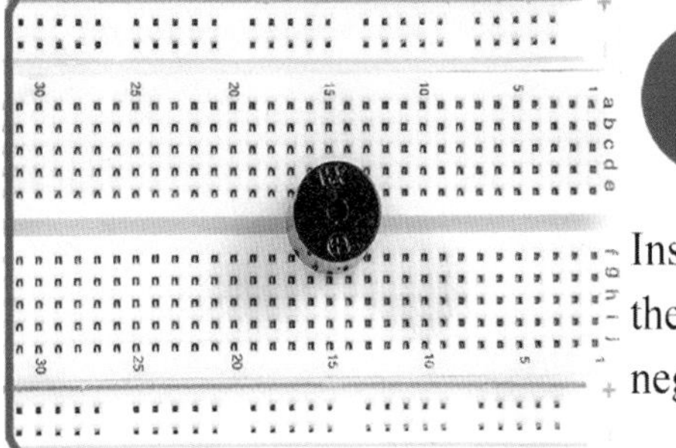

9.1

Insert the positive pin of a DC Buzzer into the meeting point of f and 15 and the negative pin at the meeting point of e and 15.

9.2

Put the positive pin of the red LED bulb at the meeting point of f and 25 and the negative pin of the red LED bulb into the convergence of e and 25.

9.3

Place the collector pin of a transistor at the meeting point of j and 44 and the base pin of a transistor at the meeting point of j and 45, and the emitter pin of a transistor into the intersection of j and 46.

9.4

Put one end of a 100 Ohm Resistor pin into the junction of j and 25 and the rest pin of it at the positive rail on the breadboard.

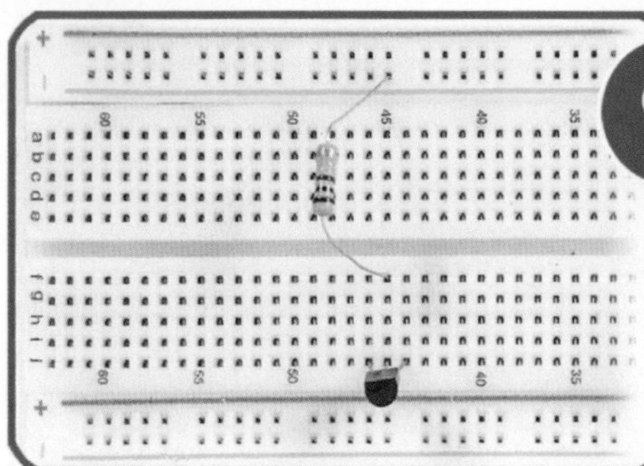

9.5

Put one end of a 2.7K Ohm Resistor pin into the junction of f and 45 and the rest pin of it at the negative rail on the breadboard.

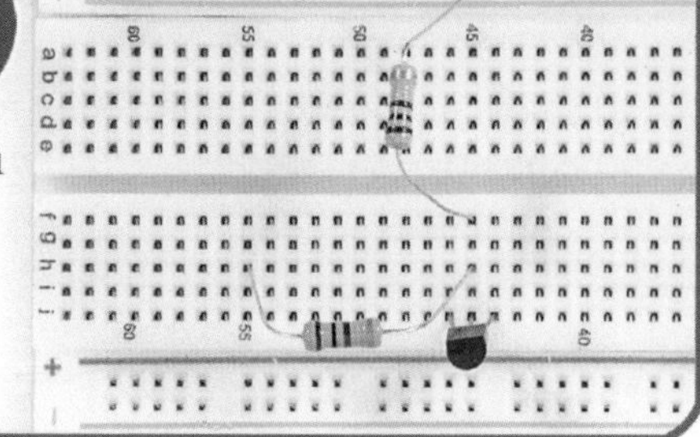

9.6

Put one end of a 100 Ohm Resistor pin at the meeting point of h and 45 and the rest pin of it at the meeting point of h and 55.

9.7

Insert one end of a wire into the meeting point of h and 15 and the other end into the meeting point of h and 25.

9.8

Insert one end of a wire into the meeting point of b and 15 and the other end into the meeting point of b and 25.

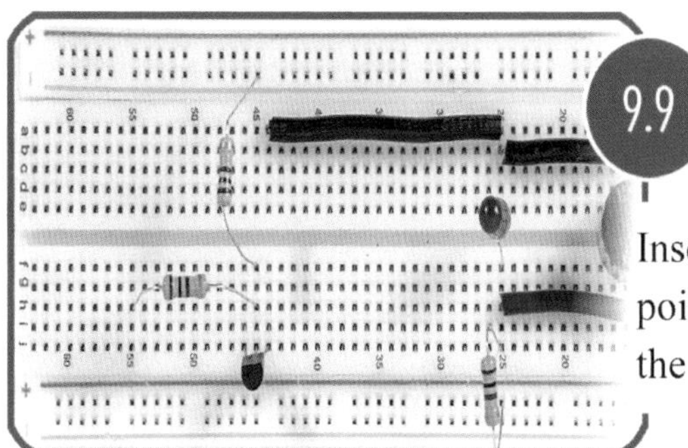

9.9

Insert one end of a wire into the meeting point of a and 25 and the other end into the meeting point of a and 44.

9.10

Insert one end of a wire into the meeting point of i and 44 and the other end into the meeting point of b and 44.

9.11

Insert one end of a wire into the meeting point of f and 46 and the other end into the negative rail on the breadboard.

9.12

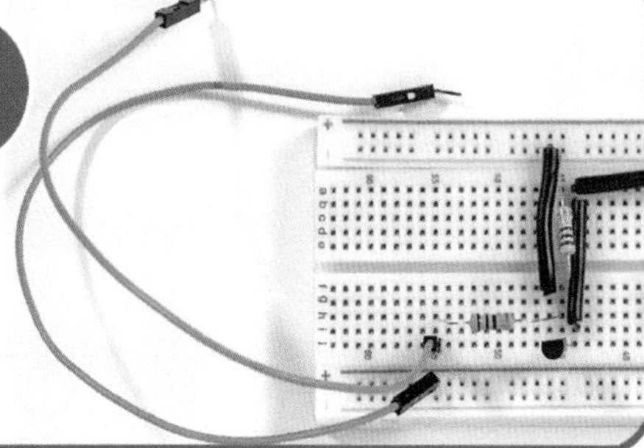

Insert one wire into the meeting point of j and 55. And then, insert another wire into the positive rail on the breadboard.

9.13

Connect a 9V battery to the battery connector, and then connect the positive wire of the battery connector to the positive rail on the breadboard and the negative wire of the battery connector to the negative rail on the breadboard.

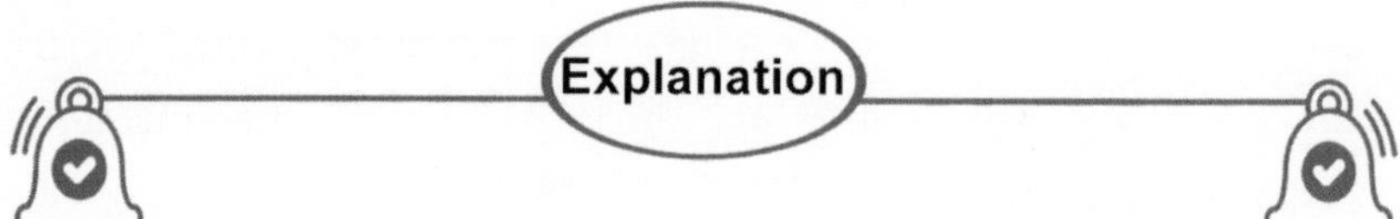

Figures 9.1 to 9.6 are the placement of components and Figures 9.7 to 9.13 are the figures of wiring the components. Figure 9.12 shows the two wires to put into a cup or tank. If the two pieces of wire are put into a cup or tank, when the water is full, both ends of the two pieces of wire will be in contact with the surface of the water, and the lights will light up, and the sound will be alarmed. The LED and DC Buzzer are connected to the collector of the transistor and the emitter of the transistor is grounded.

PROJECT (10)
Music Reactive LEDs circuit

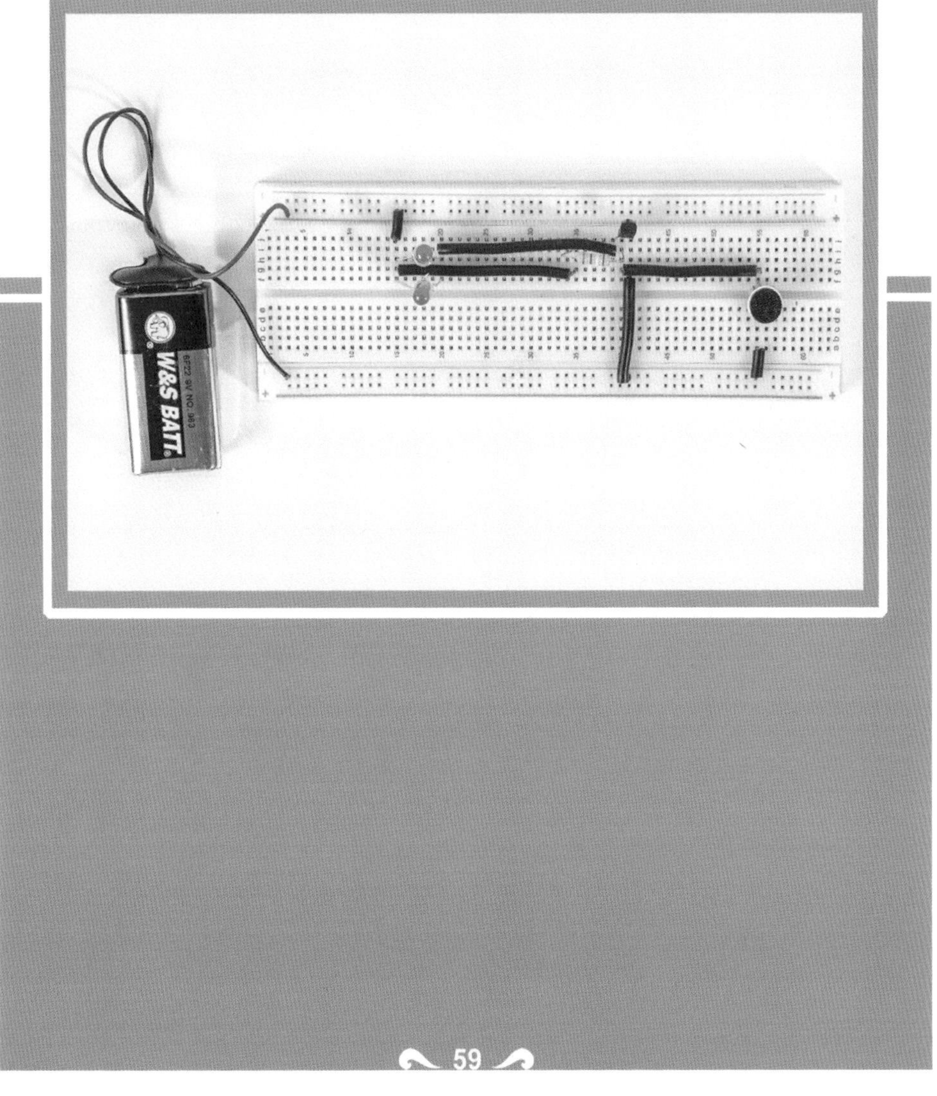

COMPONENTS

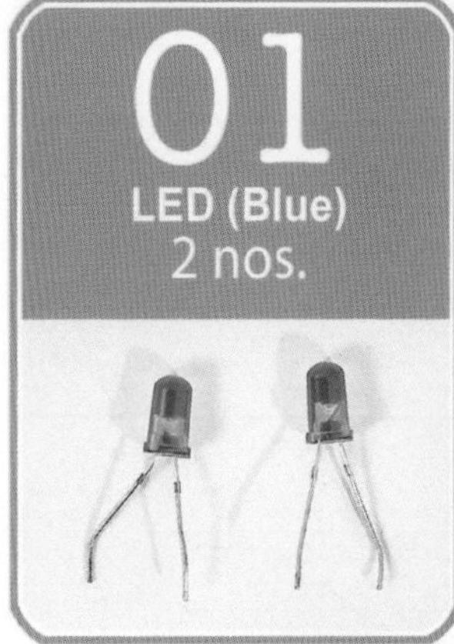
01
LED (Blue)
2 nos.

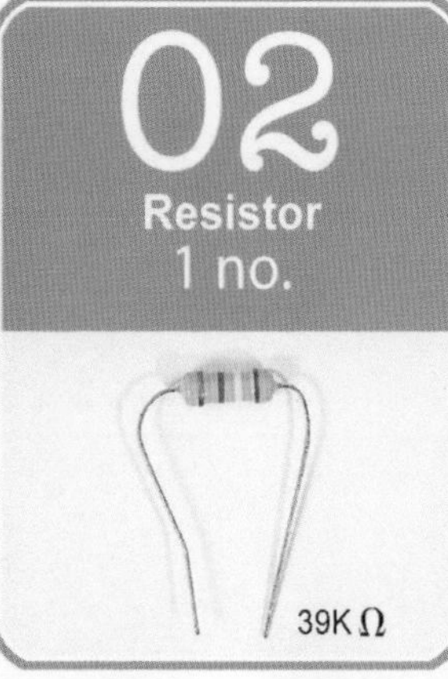
02
Resistor
1 no.
39K Ω

03
Mic
1 no.

04
Transistor BC 547
1 no.

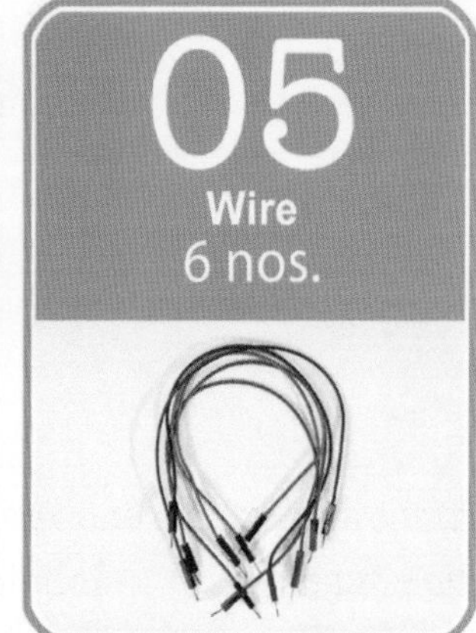
05
Wire
6 nos.

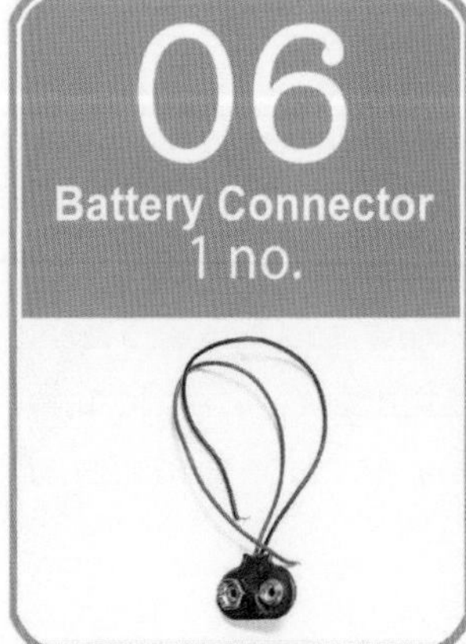
06
Battery Connector
1 no.

07
Battery 9V
1 no.
6F22 9V NO. 963
W&S BATT.

08
Breadboard
1 no.

Steps of Implementation

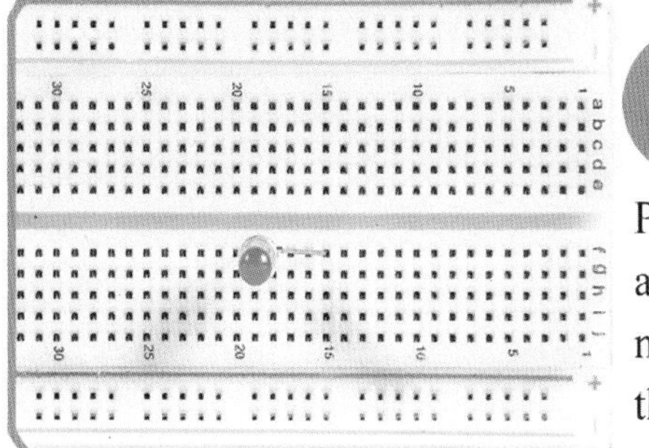

10.1

Put the positive pin of the blue LED bulb at the meeting point of f and 15 and the negative pin of the blue LED bulb into the convergence of f and 20.

10.2

Put the positive pin of the blue LED bulb at the meeting point of h and 15 and the negative pin of the blue LED bulb into the convergence of h and 20.

10.3

Place the collector pin of a transistor at the meeting point of j and 39 and the base pin of a transistor at the meeting point of j and 40, and the emitter pin of a transistor into the intersection of j and 41.

10.4

Put one end of a 39K Ohm Resistor pin at the meeting point of h and 35 and the rest pin of it at the meeting point of h and 40.

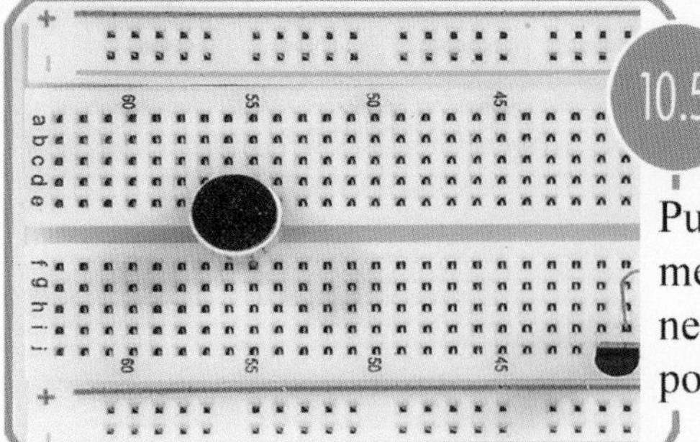

10.5

Put a positive pin of a mic at the meeting point of f and 55 and a negative pin of it into the meeting point of e and 55.

10.6

Insert one end of a wire into the meeting point of j and 15 and the other end into the positive rail on the breadboard.

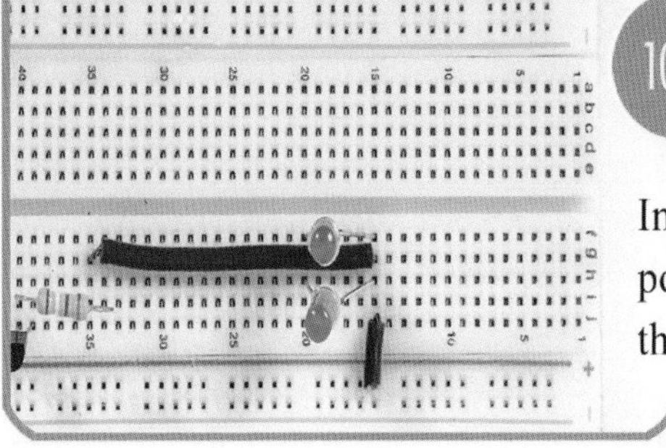

10.7

Insert one end of a wire into the meeting point of g and 15 and the other end into the meeting point of g and 35.

10.8

Insert one end of a wire into the meeting point of i and 20 and the other end into the meeting point of i and 39.

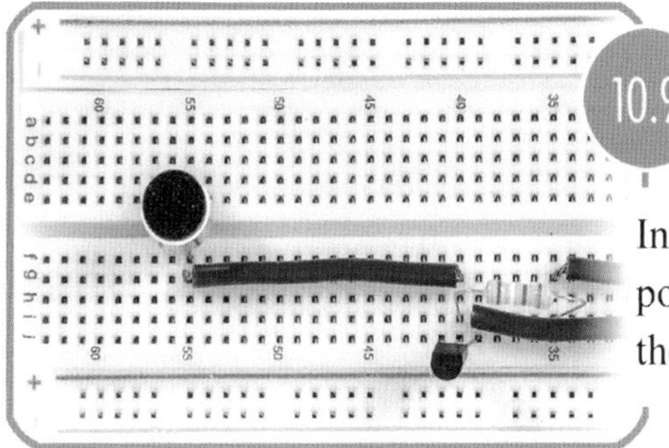

10.9

Insert one end of a wire into the meeting point of g and 40 and the other end into the meeting point of g and 55.

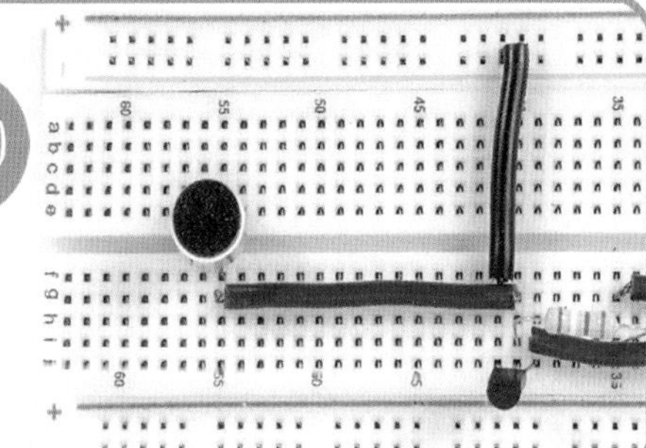

10.10

Insert one end of a wire into the meeting point of f and 41 and the other end into the negative rail on the breadboard.

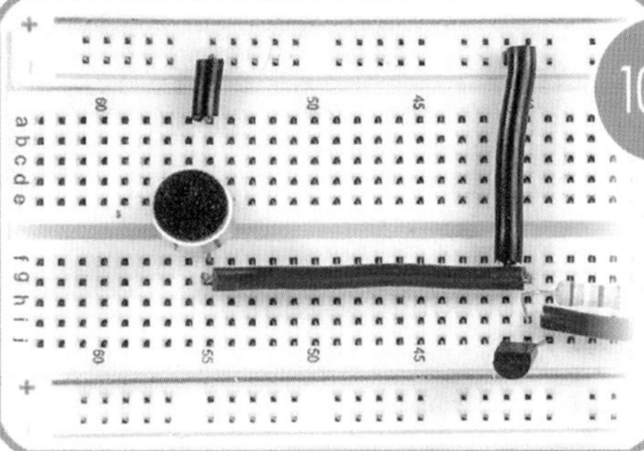

10.11

Insert one end of a wire into the meeting point of a and 55 and the other end into the negative rail on the breadboard.

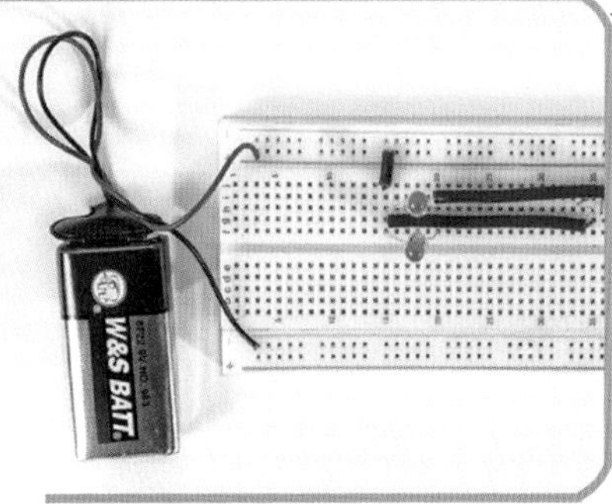

10.12

Connect a 9V battery to the battery connector, and then connect the positive wire of the battery connector to the positive rail on the breadboard and the negative wire of the battery connector to the negative rail on the breadboard.

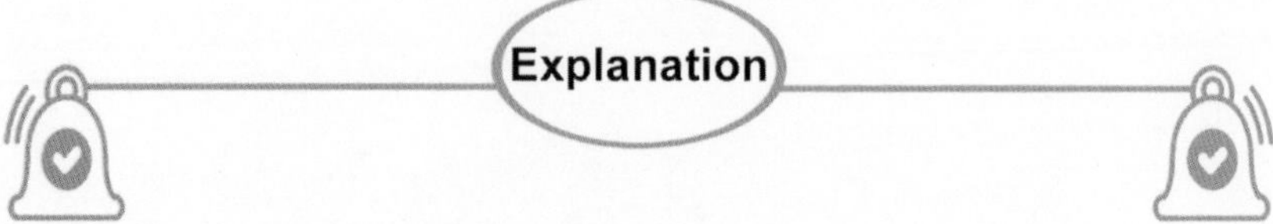

Figures 10.1 to 10.5 are the placement of components and
Figures 10.6 to 10.12 are the figures of wiring
the components.
The LEDs will light up according to the sound vibration
when placing a mic on the breadboard close to phone speaker
or a player speaker playing a music.
Two LEDs bulbs are connected in parallel,
and connected to the collector of a transistor.
The mic is connected to the emitter of the transistor.

Printed in Great Britain
by Amazon

51811556R00039